CW00407590

Exploring the lanoscape of The National Forest

A walkers' guide to the landscape and natural environment of The National Forest

by

Keith Ambrose, Annette McGrath, Gill Weightman, Poul Strange, Sam Lattaway, Graham Lott, David Barrett, Stephen Dean and Peter Liddle

British Geological Survey, Keyworth, Nicker Hill, Nottingham NG12 5GG ☎ 0115 936 3100

Contents

Bibliographic reference:

AMBROSE, K, McGRATH, A, WEIGHTMAN, G, STRANGE, P, LATTAWAY, S, LOTT, G, BARRETT, D, DEAN, S, and LIDDLE, P. 2012. *Exploring the landscape of The National Forest. A walkers' guide to the landscape and natural environment of The National Forest.* Keyworth, Nottingham: British Geological Survey.

WELCOME TO THE NATIONAL FOREST

Photograph © Lesley Hextall, courtesy of NFC

Calke autumn colours.

The National Forest offers a variety of landscape types, from extensive gently undulating clay lowlands dominated by mixed farming, to the hilly *sandstone*[1] region in the central part. The coalfields, in Leicestershire and South Derbyshire, most notably demonstrate the great impact of man's influence on the landscape. In the east Charnwood Forest, with its rolling hills and craggy knolls, presents us with a unique landscape that has been moulded over 600 million years. The rocks here date back to the Precambrian and contain some of the oldest known fossils. This book and map will help you to explore the region: its geology, landscape, biodiversity, archaeology and industrial and cultural heritage through a series of walks. You will have a fascinating glimpse of past variations in climate that show how England has moved around on the surface of the Earth by plate tectonics. There is evidence of a turbulent geological history that has included volcanoes, mountains, major earthquakes, rainforests, rivers, lakes, seas, deserts and glaciers.

The book will also demonstrate how the geology of The National Forest has had a profound influence on the economy of the area, dating back over the centuries, with many industries largely dependent on the natural resources. Some are now no longer viable, such as coal mining, iron ore and lime, but others such as aggregate extraction, gypsum and brick clays, are still very prosperous. The effect of these industries has been to significantly change the landscape in many areas, most notably in the coalfields, but also the extensive aggregate extraction in Charnwood Forest.

---

1   Italicised words are explained in the Glossary.

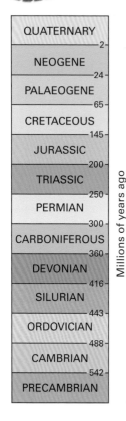

Periods of geological time.

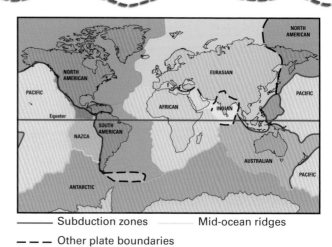

——— Subduction zones ——— Mid-ocean ridges

– – – Other plate boundaries

Tectonic plates of the world.

WALKING IN THE NATIONAL FOREST

We have selected walks from rights of way, mainly over easy terrain and use recognised footpaths or designated recreation areas. They will help you to see the geology and its relation to the biodiversity, archaeology, and cultural and industrial heritage of the Forest. Apart from in Charnwood Forest, there are few rock exposures.

When out walking, always take a map (Ordnance Survey 1:50 000 scale Landranger Sheets 128, 129, and 140, and 1:25 000 scale Explorer sheets, ADD 245, 246, 232 and 233); a compass or GPS might be useful. Wear sturdy outdoor footwear

(some of the paths are very muddy in wet weather), and carry clothing to suit the time of year and the likelihood of changes in the weather. Remember that some of the walks can cross over, or follow, busy country roads. Always respect the Country Code and, if you have a dog, make sure it is on a lead. Finally, always remember:

'leave only footprints; take only photographs'

GEOLOGY

Technical terms have been avoided where possible, but those that do occur are either explained in the text, or in the **glossary** of geological terms (p.102).

Timescale

The geological age of rocks is classified according to periods of time. Fossils are used to date some rocks, and place them within one of these periods. In The National Forest, fossils are generally only found in the Carboniferous and Precambrian. Some rocks can be dated in millions or thousands of years, measured by the radioactive decay of certain elements in the minerals that they contain.

Plate tectonics

Throughout geological time, continents have moved across the Earth's surface by a mechanism known as plate tectonics. Since the Precambrian rocks of Charnwood Forest were formed over 600 million years ago, plate movements have shifted England from the southern to the northern hemisphere. In doing so, it has passed though every major climatic zone we see today, from equatorial to arctic. Throughout this journey, the land has been submerged under the sea on many occasions, but has also been raised above sea level, washed by major rivers and covered by tropical rain forest or desert. Most recently, it has been in the grip of ice ages. These changes in climate and environment have helped to create a great diversity of landscape and geology.

Tectonic plates are rigid portions of our crust that are continually moving. These movements are so slow, rarely much more than a few millimetres per year, that we cannot see them happening. However, they generate earthquakes which are sometimes felt along the zones where the plates meet. Where plates move apart (diverge), such as in the middle of the Atlantic, molten rock (magma) rises and solidifies to form new oceanic crust. In England we are a long way from a plate boundary and so the incidence of earthquakes is very low; when they do occur, they are generally insignificant, causing little damage.

Precambrian — volcanoes, seas and the dawn of life

The Precambrian rocks of Charnwood Forest are some of the oldest in England. They were formed when England was in the southern hemisphere, located along an immense structure called a *subduction zone*. This was the meeting point between two colliding tectonic plates, one of which was forced down beneath the other. This caused the rocks to melt at depth; the resulting magma rose to the surface, forming a chain of active volcanoes surrounded by the sea — known as an island arc. These volcanoes were very violent and explosive. They produced virtually no lava flows that we can see, but spewed out huge amounts of ash, accompanied by solid but red-hot debris that avalanched down the slopes of the volcanoes and into the sea as *pyroclastic flows*. The fine-grained ash settled on the sea floor after falling out from the air, amassing a great thickness of volcanic (or *volcaniclastic*) material (at least 3.5 km) forming a sequence of rocks known as the **Charnian Supergroup**. The active volcano on the island of Montserrat in the Caribbean is thought to be a modern-day

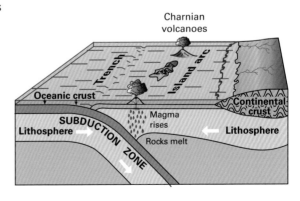

Reconstruction of the Precambrian subduction zone beneath England and Wales.

Pyroclastic flow cascades down the mountain side of the Soufrière Hills volcano on Montserrat.

Old John Tower in Bradgate Park with well-bedded tuffs in the foreground.

example of how the Precambrian volcano of Charnwood Forest would have erupted.

The volcanic debris formed layers of sediment in the sea which hardened over time to form rocks that we know as *tuffs* (Walk 4). One of the most spectacular finds in these rocks has been the discovery of primitive marine organisms. These impressions are amongst the oldest known fossils in the world and many, such as *Charniodiscus concentricus* and *Charnia masoni*, have been named after the Charnwood Forest area.

Late in the Precambrian, the volcanic magma chambers cooled very slowly at depth, forming *intrusions* of coarse grained *igneous rocks* — the **North and South Charnwood Diorites**. The South Charnwood Diorites were originally named Markfieldite, after the village of Markfield where they occur.

Eventually, subduction stopped, the volcanoes ceased erupting and erosion began to wear them down. A subdued, low-lying landscape resulted, enabling the

Charnia masoni, the first fossil to be found in Charnwood Forest.

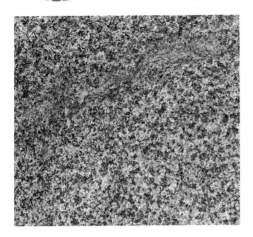

Polished slab of South Charnwood Diorite — 'Markfieldite'.

sea to advance across the region in early Cambrian times. The sea floor was made up of sands and muds washed in by rivers from the nearby land. These compacted to form layers of *sedimentary rocks* that we call the **Swithland Slates**.

The Swithland Slates were originally thought to be of Precambrian age, but recent discoveries of *trace fossils* in Swithland Slate show evidence of burrowing activity by sea-floor animals. This has led geologists to revise their age to the younger Cambrian period, about 530 million years ago. You may be able to see these fossils on Swithland Slate gravestones in Ratby churchyard [SK5129 0593], on the southern side of Charnwood Forest. You can easily tell the Swithland Slate gravestones by their very rough back surface compared to the smooth Welsh slate gravestones.

The rocks of Charnwood Forest and several more walks in that area are described in the companion book: 'Exploring the Landscape of Charnwood Forest and Mountsorrel', published by the British Geological Survey.

Silurian and Devonian — orogeny, and the Caledonides mountain belt

Mountain building, or 'orogeny', is one of the more dramatic events in geological history. It occurs when two continental plates collide, and one is driven down, or subducts, beneath the other as is happening along the Himalayan mountain chain today. During this event, the rocks become heated up and compressed, a process called metamorphism. In Charnwood Forest, we can see evidence of a major mountain building event at the end of the Silurian Period, about 420 million years ago, during the final stages of the **Caledonian Orogeny**. One feature

Swithland slate quarry in Swithland Wood. Note the cleavage.

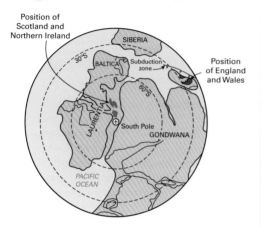

Position of various parts of the British Isles during Ordovician times.

Photograph © Annette McGrath, courtesy of NFC

Cleavage and bedding in the Hallgate Member, Bradgate Park.

produced by this process of compression is cleavage — a series of generally near-vertical subparallel fractures in the rock, caused by the crystallisation of new minerals with a parallel alignment at right angles to the direction of maximum pressure. Typically, rocks with a cleavage will break easily along these surfaces. It can be seen in all Charnian rocks but is particularly well developed in the Swithland Slates (p.22).

Carboniferous — *warm seas and coral reefs, deltas and rainforests*

When our story started, England and Scotland were a long way apart. By Carboniferous times, they were joined together and very close to the Equator where they became partially covered by warm tropical seas. The resulting sediments formed the rocks we know as the **Peak Limestone**. Many of these rocks are rich in fossil corals and shells (brachiopods) that can be seen at Grace Dieu and Ticknall. (Walk 10). The best exposures are just outside of the Forest, at Breedon (Walk 3) and Cloud Hill quarries where there are

viewing platforms. Much of the original *limestone* has been altered, converting the calcium-rich mineral calcite into the magnesium-rich mineral dolomite and the rocks into dolostones. At this time, the Carboniferous sea lapped onto Charnwood Forest which was still standing up as a mountain range.

Slightly later in the Carboniferous, the sea level fell and large rivers washed over the area, forming major deltas like that of the Mississippi. Sandstones of the Millstone Grit were deposited, which can be seen around Melbourne and at Carver's Rocks (Walks 3 and 6). At times, the sea level rose and the deltas became submerged. The muds that were deposited yield fossils including a class of molluscs (cephalopods) called goniatites that were related to the ammonites. In the town of Melbourne, you can see the Millstone Grit sandstones in many buildings and walls. It is also exposed

Carboniferous limestone at Grace Dieu quarry.

around the Staunton Harold reservoir visitor centre and at Carver's Rocks.

At the end of the Carboniferous, the environment was hot and humid. Vegetation flourished and much of England was covered with equatorial rainforests just as we see in the Congo or Amazon regions today. Thick piles of rotting vegetation accumulated and over time became deeply buried and compressed to form the coal seams of the local coalfields. The Coal Measures are very diverse and contain an abundance of fossilised plant remains. They are important for the natural resources — coal, ironstone, fireclay — that fuelled the Industrial Revolution. The landscape of The National Forest was dramatically shaped by the extraction of these resources in the 19th and 20th centuries.

Periodically, sea level rose and flooded the land. We know this by the presence of marine fossils in thin beds of mudstone. The end of the Carboniferous Period was marked by another episode of earth movements, known as the **Variscan Orogeny**. This

Sphenopteris, a typical fossil plant from the Coal Measures.

Breedon Hill

Charnwood Forest

Reconstruction of the Triassic braided river flowing around Charnwood Forest.

resulted in the formation of the vast supercontinent of Pangaea. Evidence of these earth movements can be seen from the viewpoints overlooking Breedon (Walk 3) and Cloud Hill quarries, where the rocks are tilted and dip very steeply westwards.

Permian and Triassic — deserts and rivers

Following the humid Carboniferous, the Permian Period was very arid and represents a major period of erosion lasting for at least 40 million years. Many of the Carboniferous rocks were stripped

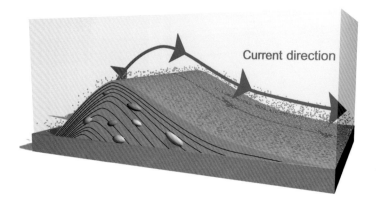

Current direction

Formation of sand dunes on the river bed in relation to the current flow. This shows how the inclination of the cross-bedding in rocks gives the direction of flow of the river that deposited them.

Photograph © Saudi Geological Survey. P R Johnson

Charnwood Forest and Mountsorrel could have resembled this Arabian landscape (Nabitah fault zone east of Bishah, Saudi Arabia) in Permian and Triassic times.

away and Charnwood Forest was reduced to a range of barren mountains. The debris from this erosion can be found in rocks of the **Moira Formation**, preserved along much of the northern and western flanks of the Carboniferous outcrop.

Erosion during the Permian resulted in a low-lying landscape at the start of the succeeding Triassic period. In the earliest part of the Triassic, much of England was drained by a major river that flowed northwards from France, skirting around the rugged hills of Charnwood Forest. In its early stages, the river was fast-flowing with many branching channels depositing coarse sands and gravels (a braided system). Later, as the flow waned, it developed a more meandering course, depositing finer sediments. In The National Forest, the deposits of this river are seen as sandstones and *conglomerates*. These rocks occur between Burton upon Trent and Melbourne and are known as

the **Kidderminster** and **Bromsgrove Sandstone formations**. Along the northern fringes of Charnwood Forest, the **Shepshed Sandstone** represents the sediments of more local tributary streams

2 cm

Cubes that were originally salt crystals but have since been replaced by sediment in the Mercia Mudstone.

that carried pebbles of Charnian rocks into the main river. Where these rocks are exposed (Walks 1 and 6) and where they have been used as building stones, you will be able to see *cross-bedding*. This feature was formed by underwater sand dunes that migrated down-current along the river bed and it recorded the direction in which the river was flowing; in The National Forest this was towards the north and north-east.

Later in the Triassic, when England had moved to a position about 20° north of the Equator, a vast desert developed across Pangaea. It is thought that the climate resembled that of modern-day Saudi Arabia.

Seams of gypsum in the Mercia Mudstone. The seam mined at the Fauld mine is about the thickness of the entire face.

Photograph © BGS

It was not a sandy desert, but was dominated by fine, wind-borne (aeolian) dust. After burial and compaction, this material was transformed into the red mudstones and *siltstones* of the **Mercia Mudstone Group**. Just as in modern deserts, cloudbursts periodically caused flash floods that covered large areas of the flat desert, depositing thin layers of greenish grey sandstone or siltstone. As the water evaporated, temporary lakes formed, known as playas.

The landscape was now predominantly very flat, but Charnwood Forest continued to stand up as low hills. Other hills, such as Breedon and Mountsorrel, stood up above the low-lying ground as islands (known as inselbergs). The sea was not far away and periodically, parts of the land subsided below sea level. Subsidence due to faulting happened on the west side of The National Forest in an area known as the Needwood Basin, where thick Triassic sediments were deposited. When the sea flooded the land it was very shallow and the evaporation rate was high, enriching the water with dissolved salts. As the concentrations increased, rock salt, or halite, precipitated out and formed

layers within the mudstones. We don't see halite at the surface but we know it is there from boreholes drilled in the area. At Hanbury 30 m of halite is interbedded with mudstone, about 150 m below the surface. At other times, rivers deposited sandstones of the **Arden Sandstone Formation** and **Cotgrave Sandstone Member**. You can see the former exposed in an old quarry at Tatenhill, just south-west of Burton upon Trent. We know from cross-bedding in other areas of England that this river was flowing eastwards.

The Mercia Mudstone Group of the East Midlands contains thick deposits of gypsum (p.15). The main seam is the **Tutbury Gypsum** which varies in thickness from about 1 to 5 m. It was formed by the evaporation of saline water just beneath the sediment surface. Gypsum is common throughout the Mercia Mudstone Group.

Because the Triassic climate was very arid, plants and animals had little chance of being preserved as fossils. Some reptile bones, sharks' teeth, burrows (trace fossils) and crustaceans have, however, been found. One reptile living at this time left only footprints,

Chirotherium, preserved in the sandstone. One of these footprints has been found in the **Tarporley Siltstone Formation** at Newhurst Quarry near Shepshed. Plant spores have also been found in some rocks and have been used to date them.

By the end of the Triassic Period, the Charnwood Hills and Breedon Hill had been buried under sediment, reducing the landscape to a low-lying plain close to sea level. The area continued to subside and a warm, tropical sea advanced across the whole area. The first indication of this *marine transgression* is a unit called the **Blue Anchor Formation**, with its distinctive greenish grey siltstones and mudstones. When fully marine conditions were established, dark grey, fossiliferous mudstones of the **Westbury Formation,** were deposited. These two rock units can be found at the western end of the Forest around Newchurch, and just outside at Marchington Cliff.

The rugged nature of the Charnwood hills and steep dips of the Charnian rocks resulted in a very uneven and spectacular contact between the Triassic and the older rocks. This contact, known as an *erosional unconformity,* can be seen in many of the quarries in Charnwood Forest. You may also be able to see some deeply carved channels that are known as wadis. In Charnwood Forest, the unconformity represents a time gap of around 350 million years. Where the Triassic overlies the younger Carboniferous rocks, the interval is about 110 million years.

Jurassic and Cretaceous — tropical seas

The Jurassic Period was characterised by fully marine environments that lasted throughout most of the next 140 million years up to the end of the Cretaceous. During this time, a considerable thickness of fossiliferous mudstones and limestones was deposited but due to later erosion,

Ancient wadi infilled with red Triassic sediments, New Cliffe Hill (Stanton) Quarry.

none of these rocks are preserved in The National Forest. The nearest outcrops are in and to the east of Leicester. At the end of the Cretaceous Period, the land was uplifted and the sea withdrew from this area. These movements were related to the final break-up of the supercontintent of Pangaea. Britain now occupied the margin of the Eurasian Plate which continued to 'drift' northwards. A period of intense erosion removed all of the Jurassic, and Cretaceous as well as parts of the Triassic succession from The National Forest to reveal the older rocks.

Quaternary — the Great Ice Age

Sediments of Quaternary age, including modern times, are referred to as superficial deposits. The last great geological event affecting England happened in the Pleistocene Period, around 2 million years ago. During this period, our climate changed from warmer than today to very cold Arctic conditions. Scientists have been able to accurately plot the dates of these climate changes by measuring oxygen isotopes in deep-sea sediments. They show several very cold periods that we call the ice ages, but we can find evidence of only two glaciations in The National Forest. The first occurred during the Anglian Quaternary Stage, about 440 000 years ago, when ice sheets covered most of England.

As the ice sheets melted they left behind debris which we call till or boulder clay. They also left sands and gravels deposited by melting waters from the ice sheet, as well as laminated clays that were deposited in lakes in front of the melting ice. Two

Typical Thrussington Till.

Woolly mammoths and rhinos like this may have roamed around The National Forest thousands of years ago. Inset: Typical fossil bones representing animals seen in the ice ages, including woolly mammoth tusk and reindeer antler.

ice sheets were involved, each producing a distinctive type of till. The Thrussington Till was deposited by ice that travelled from the north-west and carried red clay-rich material derived mainly from the Triassic Mercia Mudstone together with Carboniferous rocks. A later ice sheet deposited the Oadby Till, from the north-east. This till is grey, due to a high content of Jurassic mudstone. It also contains common fragments of Cretaceous flint and chalk.

The second ice age to produce deposits in this area occurred during the Quaternary Devensian, between about 30 000 and 15 000 years ago. This ice sheet only covered parts of England but just crept eastwards into The National Forest, to Burton upon Trent. Rather surprisingly,

we see very little evidence of landforms associated with this recent glaciation but there is clearly a younger layer of glacial till on the surface. This till is brown to red-brown in colour and resembles the earliest Thrussington Till of the Anglian ice sheet. Away from this ice sheet, the climate was extremely cold and tundra-like, producing what we know as a *periglacial* environment. England was populated by animals such as woolly mammoth, woolly rhinoceros and reindeer, some of which are now extinct. Fossil remains of these animals, including bones, tusks, teeth and antlers, have been found in the Trent valley river gravels around Burton upon Trent.

The Trent, a major river in the Pleistocene Period, has changed its course many times.

For example, 300 000 years ago it was approximately 30 m above the present-day river, in a much wider flood plain. At this time, the river was a fast-flowing braided system, transporting large amounts of sand and gravel that are now seen as **river terrace deposits.** These are perched on the sides of the modern Trent valley at four different levels. Today, the Trent and its tributaries flow much more slowly and tend to meander across the *floodplains*, depositing **alluvium** in the form of clay and silt. In the very recent postglacial (Holocene) period, the landscape has been further modified by processes that have deposited hill wash (**colluvium**) in valley floors and solifluction deposits (**head**) on valley sides. The melting permafrost from the last ice age produced unstable, waterlogged ground that resulted in landslides on some steep slopes although these are few in number in The National Forest.

MINERALS

A diverse range of minerals occurs in the rocks of The National Forest and originated in many different ways. *Igneous rocks* can be sources of mineral fluids and fractures in these rocks, as well as *faults,* can also act as pathways for fluids. *Unconformities* between different rock types may represent former land surfaces along which minerals may have been deposited, for example, where younger Triassic strata overlie the ancient and extensively fractured Precambrian and Carboniferous rocks.

At Bardon Hill Quarry, minerals such as native copper, and other copper minerals have been found at the unconformity between volcanic rocks and overlying Triassic sediments; the minerals are sometimes found in ancient river valleys known as wadis. There are also small occurrences of gold at Bardon Hill, Whitwick and Morley quarries. Some of the gold may be associated with igneous rocks that were forced up (intruded) into the sedimentary rocks as near-vertical sheets or dykes. Small grains of gold have been panned from the streams of northern Charnwood but these may be related to mineralisation along the Triassic unconformity.

All Photographs © Gill Weightman, courtesy of NFC

Crystals of calcite with sulphides (top); copper minerals from Bardon (middle); galena crystals in dolomitised limestone (bottom).

At Newhurst Quarry, a Site of Special Scientific Interest (SSSI) near Shepshed, there is mineralisation associated with an igneous rock called the North Charnwood Diorite, which was intruded into Precambrian sedimentary rocks. The minerals formed along joints in the *diorite* and are commonly copper-bearing. The lead sulphide mineral galena occurs in the overlying Triassic *sandstones*, their porosity allowing the easy passage of mineralising fluids. Nearby at Tickow Lane [SK462186], lead minerals were discovered by chance in Triassic Sandstones during excavations for a canal. Galena was mined there between 1865 and 1867, but no one knows what became of the ores!

Farther west, a large structure known as the Thringstone Fault forms a boundary between the older basement rocks in Charnwood Forest and the younger Carboniferous strata of the Leicestershire Coalfield. This *fault* formed a plane of weakness in the rock, providing an important passage for later migrating fluids that deposited a wide variety of minerals, including *quartz*, calcite and various iron, lead, copper and zinc minerals.

The Carboniferous *limestones* of The National Forest are very reactive rocks enabling minerals to be readily deposited. At Breedon and Cloud Hill quarries, many minerals have been found; the solution of the limestone along numerous fractures has resulted in the formation of caves and small cavities which are commonly lined with calcite crystals and various sulphides. A large mass of iron oxide mineralisation was recently uncovered in Cloud Hill Quarry and is associated with the Triassic unconformity.

Some examples of minerals from The National Forest can be seen on display in the Extractive Industries Gallery at Snibston Discovery Park, Coalville.

Gypsum

Gypsum has been mined around Fauld and Hanbury (Walk 5) since the 12th century. This soft, chalky-looking mineral is used to make several products, including plaster of Paris, but a stronger, crystalline type known as alabaster is famous as an ornamental stone. Some National Forest churches contain carvings, memorials and tombs made from alabaster, especially in the western part of the Forest. The seam worked for this purpose is the Tutbury Gypsum, which is 6 m thick at Fauld. Gypsum (calcium sulphate $CaSO_4.2H_2O$) is actually only found at or close to the surface. Underground, the compound found is anhydrite ($CaSO_4$, anhydrous calcium

Photograph © BPB United Kingdom Limited

Underground working at the Fauld gypsum mine.

sulphate). This was originally deposited as gypsum and was later converted to anhydrite due to the increase of pressure and temperature with depth. It then reverted back to gypsum by the addition of water after erosion had exposed the seam.

The earliest extraction of gypsum occurred between Tutbury and Draycott in the Clay with three working mines at Hanbury in 1894. The Fauld Mine started much earlier, before 1800, and is currently worked by the pillar-and-stall method. This method of mining removes only part of the resource, leaving 25 per cent of the mineral behind as roof supports (pillars) in order to minimise caving of the mine.

A school for the carving of alabaster developed in Burton upon Trent. It specialised in tombs and church monuments, and supplied many parts of Britain and Europe as long ago as 1462. It died out in the 17th century, but plenty of examples remain, such as carvings in Yoxall and Breedon churches. Farther afield, local alabaster was used for the building of Cornelius Vanderbilt's mansion in New York, USA, and local plaster was used in the ceiling of the Tower ballroom in Blackpool. One of the last uses of Fauld alabster was for a bath carved as a wedding present for Princess Margaret. Mining in the area continues to the present day, with the workings extending more than 6 km to the south, underneath The National Forest (Walk 5). The alabaster was worked out in the 1990s, and today, the mine is still worked by British Gypsum for anhydrite, used in cement manufacture.

The Fauld mine disaster

The Fauld mine had a major catastrophe during the Second World War. At about 11 am on the morning of November the

Alabaster tomb in St Peter's Church, Yoxall. It is dated 1564 and was carved in Burton.

Photograph © Robert Morris, courtesy of NFC

27th 1944, around 3500 tons of explosives in an old part of the mine, used by the RAF as a munitions store, blew up. The huge explosion was, at the time, the world's largest accidental blast and was seen or felt up to 60 km away and heard in London; it registered on seismographs across Europe. Over one million tons of rock and soil were ejected up into the sky, leaving behind a crater 250 m in diameter and 50–100 m deep. A farm sited directly above the explosion completely disappeared. Flying rocks damaged buildings nearby in Hanbury where the Cock Inn and village hall had to be completely rebuilt; other debris landed up to 10 km away. The exact death toll is uncertain but up to 90 were reported dead or missing, and 200 cattle were killed.

WATER RESOURCES

Rivers and springs are the most obvious supplies of water, but it can also come from rocks that are permeable and therefore suitable for storing and transmitting groundwater — known as aquifers. The best are the *sandstones* and *conglomerates* that occur at depth. They typically need layers of impervious rocks (rocks that do not store or

Southern part of Staunton Harold reservoir.

transmit water), such as *mudstone*, to contain them. Well-fractured rocks can also form good *aquifers*. One of the

Disused water tower beside a Swithland Slate quarry in Swithland Wood.

most important aquifers in England is the Sherwood Sandstone Group, and in The National Forest this supplies many towns and villages. It also supplies the brewing industry of Burton upon Trent (p.35). Other rock formations can supply small amounts of water, such as the Arden Sandstone, Cotgrave Sandstone and Tarporley Siltstone from the Mercia Mudstone Group; the thicker sandstone *beds* of the Millstone Grit and Coal Measures, and the Carboniferous *limestone*. The latter is an important aquifer in parts of the country but not in The National Forest. The other main source is the various river terrace deposits along the River Trent. These consist of highly porous sand and gravel and are therefore ideal aquifers. Groundwater from the Trent gravels around Burton contains high calcium and sulphate concentrations due to the dissolution of gypsum in the underlying Mercia Mudstone. This means that it is also ideal for the brewing industry supplementing the supplies from deeper wells.

Man's influence has created artificial water storage facilites. Underground, the abandoned mines of the local coalfield can store considerable quantities of water but it is commonly polluted. Above ground, there are five main reservoirs in The National Forest, at Blackbrook, Cropston, Thornton, Foremark and Staunton Harold.

COALFIELDS

The importance of coal mining to the industrial heritage of The National Forest cannot be overstated, as the exploitation and extraction of 'King Coal' was once the mainstay of the local economy. Coal mining was fundamental to the economic development of the area and fashioned both the landscape and the way of daily life.

Coal mining in The National Forest, dates back to Roman times. The first irrefutable records date to the 13th century in Swannington (1204) and Swadlincote in 1290, 1374 and 1377. During the 15th and 16th centuries, coal was extracted in situ; when a seam cropped out at the surface it was dug out in opencast workings.

A **bell pit** is a primitive method of mining coal, iron ore or other minerals

Willesley opencast pit, in 1971.

where these lie near to the surface. A shaft is sunk to the mineral which is then excavated by miners, using a winch to raise it to the surface. The name comes from the pit's cross-section, which resembles a bell. Usually there were no supports and mining continued outwards until the cavity became too dangerous or collapsed. At this point, another mine was started, usually very close by. This type of mining dates back to prehistoric times and was common in the Middle Ages. A few continued in use until the early 20th century in parts of England. The remains of bell pits can be seen as depressions left when they collapsed, commonly surrounded by small piles of spoil (Walk 7). Recent excavations in the Coleorton area have uncovered evidence of more sophisticated deep-mining techniques, using timber-lined shafts, dating from the 1450s, the earliest known in Britain.

The demand for coal greatly increased during the Elizabethan period, due to a large population growth and a shortage of timber. The coal pits in the Coleorton–Swannington area expanded and records from the time report that colliers far out-numbered all other occupations in the district. The industry continued to grow throughout the 18th century, reaching new heights in the 19th century, due to the Industrial Revolution. However, the lack of good transport links in the region hampered growth of the industry until the early 19th century, when the Ashby Canal was built. The coming of the railways during the 19th century further expanded the coal industry.

In 1831, the extension of the coalfield beneath the Triassic cover was proved and Snibston colliery opened, served by the Leicester to Swannington Railway, transporting coal to the major market of Leicester. Miners came to the area from County Durham to work at the colliery, the settlement around Snibston growing into the new town of Coalville. Snibston Colliery closed down in 1984, but is now an interactive museum of science and industry, with tours of the colliery buildings and the historic colliery railway.

At the end of the 19th century the local coalfield had an output of three million tons of coal per year, or one per cent of national production. Coal mines were taken under government control during First World War and Second World War, and in 1947 the coal industry was nationalised, which triggered the closure of many of the smaller pits. Large sums of money were injected into the eleven remaining large collieries in order to improve productivity. The modern form of 'longwall retreat' mining together with the first computer-controlled operations was pioneered in this area. Bagworth Colliery featured in the 1975 Guinness Book of Records as the most productive mine in Britain. Further closures began in the 1980s and after the National Miners' Strike of 1984–85 a massive programme of pit closures began. All collieries closed over successive years; Bagworth was the last of the traditional deep coal mines to close in Leicestershire, in 1991.

Operations moved towards opencast methods, with much of the coalfield being worked and large quantities of coal extracted. Many of the sites have been restored creating a mixture of agricultural land, woodland, meadows and open water habitats (Walks 2 and 7).

IRON ORE

Ironstone occurs at several levels in the Leicestershire and South Derbyshire coalfields. It was worked from numerous

Diagram of a typical bell pit.

bell pits at Southwood near Dimminsdale, where there was a local smelting industry, with records going back to 1306. In the early 17th century, a smelting works was constructed in the vicinity of Lount.

The Moira collieries operated an iron furnace (the Moira Furnace) built in 1804 close to the Ashby Canal (Walk 2), for smelting iron ores brought in from the local mines by canal. *Limestone* needed for the smelting process was brought in by tramway and canal from Ticknall (p.28). The industry produced mainly wrought iron goods but was unsuccessful and closed in 1807. An attempt was made to reopen it in 1810 but it was soon abandoned as a failure. However, the foundry continued to flourish, becoming the main workshop for the Earl of Moira's collieries. It eventually closed in the 1850s.

AGGREGATE INDUSTRY

Stone from Charnwood Forest has been quarried for many thousands of years. These early uses of Charnian stone are documented on page 29.

The aggregate industry was boosted by the invention of 'granite Macadam' (now known as tarmac). The abolition of the turnpikes in 1827 encouraged greater use of the roads, which in turn required additional maintenance. A second turning point was the Local Government Act in 1888 making local authorities responsible for the maintenance of their own roads. Demand for hard rock was further boosted in the 19th century by the construction of the railways. Such changes led to the opening of new hard rock quarries in Charnwood Forest.

By 1890 Charnwood Forest stone had become the main source of aggregates for the country, from the Midlands southwards, with Leicestershire producing over a million tonnes per year by 1900.

Today, Leicestershire has the only reserves of hard rock suitable for roadstone in the south of England and therefore provides the nearest and cheapest rock resources to these ever-expanding markets. The latest available production

Aerial view of New Cliff Hill (Stanton) Quarry. This quarry has now ceased working and is being backfilled with overburden from Old Cliffe Hill Quarry which has reopened. Today, 'New' Cliffe Hill is referred to as 'Stanton Quarry' and 'Old' Cliffe Hill simply as 'Cliffe Hill'.

figures are for 2008, when Leicestershire's total production of *igneous* rock was 13 446 000 tonnes. This comes from four large quarrying operations at Cliffe Hill, Bardon, Mountsorrel and Croft. Between 1997 and 2006, Leicestershire igneous rock represented 44–49 per cent of the East Midlands' total crushed rock production and about 30 per cent of Great Britain's total igneous rock production.

Lorry being filled with crushed aggregate, Cloud Hill Quarry.

Today, Bardon Hill and Cliffe Hill are the only quarries to operate within The National Forest, whilst older quarries are either undergoing restoration or have been 'mothballed'. The quarry industry has been vital to the socio-economic development of the Charnwood area of The National Forest for well over a century now, and will continue to be so for at least another 50 years. Abandoned quarries often become a positive feature of the landscape, as with age they produce a wealth of geodiversity features and varied habitats for wildlife and plants, as well as providing a multitude of recreational uses.

Extensive quarrying for sand and gravel aggregates has also taken place in Staffordshire along the Trent valley to the south of Burton upon Trent. The quarries here work the river terrace deposits. Outcrops of sand and gravel deposited by melting ice throughout The National Forest have also been worked on a small scale in the past.

LEICESTERSHIRE SLATE INDUSTRY

The use of Swithland Slate for building dates back to Roman times (p.32). In the 14th century, Borough Records show that it was used to roof major buildings in Leicester. The actual locations of the slate quarries are first cited in 1343, when the

Sand and gravel workings in the Trent Valley at Newbold.

The Brand, Groby and Woodhouse Eaves (Walk 4). By then, Swithland Slate was used for a multitude of purposes, including the manufacture of roofing slates, headstones, milestones, sundials, gateposts, kerb-edging and some household items. Traditionally the slates were laid on a roof in sizes that reduced from eaves to ridge, thus enabling even the smallest pieces of slate to be used.

Slates from the Swithland quarries tend to be pale grey, blue-green-grey or purple in colour. In the Great Pit the best *bed* of slate was apparently only 5 m wide and almost vertical. As a result, the quarry was worked to a depth of more than 60 m.

Records indicate that three quarries existed in the Groby area between 1773 and 1829: the Groby Slate Works north of Grey Lodge at Alder Spinney, and two earlier quarries, located close to Bradgate Hill Farm and the present A50. The slates in the Groby quarries are more brittle, cleave more easily, and are greenish grey in colour.

a The Millhouse, Bardon Hill Quarry c.1910.
b Steam drilling at Bardon Hill Quarry c.1920.

quarries at Swithland and Groby Park are referred to in the Records of the Borough of Leicester 1103–1603. It is also known that Bradgate House (p.35) was roofed with Swithland Slate.

Slate was generally only used for the houses of the nobility and gentry in the late 17th and early 18th centuries. A huge increase in quarrying activity took place in the 18th and 19th centuries, when the principal slate quarries were at Swithland Wood,

Swithland slate headstones.

Great Pit, Swithland Wood.

as a result, the Swithland Slate industry went into rapid decline.

By 1887, most of the Leicestershire Slate quarries had closed, signalling the end of an era, although the Old Groby Slate Quarry continued working until March 1897. Today, recycled Swithland Slate is very much in demand for building extensions or restoration, and can command a high price.

POTTERY AND CLAY

The Coal Measures that were the foundation of the coal mining industry also contained important deposits of pottery clay in South Derbyshire. Domestic and decorative pottery was made at Ticknall from the late 15th century, although clay-pits are mentioned as far back as the 13th century. By the mid 17th century,

Some of the Woodhouse Eaves quarries are not true slates, as they actually belong to the older Precambrian Maplewell Group of the Charnian Supergroup. They did not cleave so easily as the true Swithland slates, and, as a result, their use was not so widespread. However, this distinctive deep purple slate was used locally as a building stone, a good example being the Almhouses in Woodhouse Eaves.

The Swithland Slate quarries supplied stone to local markets. The area's rivers and the later Grand Union canal opened up markets farther afield such as Lincolnshire and Northamptonshire. However, the improvements in transport-ation that allowed them to be more widely distributed also made the cheaper Welsh slates more accessible. The lifting of taxes and the coming of the railways resulted in the Welsh slates flooding the market and

Recycled Swithland slate roof tiles. Note their highly irregular form.

Ticknall was famous for the production of earthenware goods, mainly dairy ware and kitchen pots, and was a major producer of 'Midland Purple' and finely decorated Cistercian ware. However, during the 18th century, ceramics from Stoke-on-Trent started to flood the market and Ticknall's cottage industry diminished, until the last pottery closed in 1891.

The clay industry really started to expand with substantial clay extraction from the so-called 'Pottery Clays Formation' of the Coal Measures in the area around Swadlincote in the late 18th century. Clay was extracted via opencast 'clay-holes' and by 1790, robust bricks (known as 'Tough Tom') were manufactured from the local yellow clay. A pottery was then established at Church Gresley in 1793, producing large earthenware pans, known as 'pancheons' used for storing milk and cream. By 1811 seven potteries existed in the Swadlincote–Gresley–Woodville area. Sharpe's Pottery, founded in 1821, produced yellow-coloured 'Mocha Ware', in its early years. The world's first rim-flushing toilet was made here.

Following the 1848 Public Health Act, improvements in sanitation and civic hygiene created a huge demand for sanitary ware. South Derbyshire clay pipes proved to be well suited to the salt glaze required to safely transport waste to the sewage treatment works. By the late 1850s, Swadlincote potteries were producing an array of pipes and sanitary goods. The development of an improved flushing water closet in 1855 helped to establish Swadlincote as a world leader in the manufacture of sanitary ware.

Some of Swadlincote's potteries continued to produce domestic and decorative pottery. The Bretby Art Pottery produced some of the 19th century's most exotic and vibrant ceramics. This unique design of pottery was not produced after 1920 when less flamboyant styles were adopted. The pottery finally closed down in 1996. Other notable potteries include the famous blue and white Cornish ware produced by TG Green at Church Gresley (1864–2007) and Measham bargeware pottery, characterised by its treacle glaze and polychrome sprigged decoration, and specialising in colourful teapots.

The clay industry in Swadlincote went into a decline after the Second World War and many of the iconic bottle kilns were demolished. Sharpe's pottery closed in 1967 as a result of competition from the larger potteries of Stoke-on-Trent, which could afford greater investment. However, the bottle kiln at Sharpe's Pottery survived, and happily re-opened as a museum, heritage and arts centre in 2003.

BRICK AND FIRECLAY

Brickmaking was once widespread in The National Forest and old maps indicate local brickpits close to many villages. Currently, there are six localities for active brick production at Ibstock, Measham,

Sharpe's pottery visitor centre in Swadlincote.

Ibstock brick quarry working the Mercia Mudstone Group.

Heather, Desford, Ellistown and Shepshed. The pits all work the Triassic Mercia Mudstone Group, the presence of iron minerals producing the typical red brick. Most of the brickworks use the Tarporley Siltstone, which provides a good mix of micaceous *sandstones* and *mudstones* for creating a wide range of bricks. The quartz grains in the sandstone are necessary to prevent excessive shrinking during firing and the presence of mica contributes favourably to the process of vitrification (the transformation of a substance into glass) that produces a glassy bond that gives the product strength. The mineral dolomite, commonly present in the Mercia Mudstone, has the effect of producing paler bricks. The blending of different clays and importing of other materials such as fireclay, anthracite and chalk, produces bricks with different properties and colours.

Fireclays are fossil soils or seatearths that supported the vegetation that formed the coal seams. Compared to most other coalfields, the seatearths of the South Derbyshire Coalfield are unusually thick, up to 4 m, and 13 of them have been worked. Fireclay was originally extracted underground from the coal mines but with the advent of opencast coal working after the Second World War, the resource was more easily and cheaply worked. Since production was far greater than usage, large stockpiles of fireclay have been produced which continue to supply the industry today. The South Derbyshire

Coalfield supplied 35 per cent of all fireclay consumed in the country in 1998.

The term 'fireclay' is derived from an ability to resist heat. Consequently, the South Derbyshire fireclays were originally valued as *refractory* raw materials used in the manufacture of firebricks and other goods. Today they are valued for their low iron content, which produces a pale buff, strong and durable (frost resistant) brick. Vitrified clay pipe, chimney pot and flue liner production has been the mainstay of the Swadlincote area. Fireclays enhance the fired strength and minimise porosity, both properties being essential for sewerage and drainage applications.

The latest development in the brick industry of Leicestershire was the opening in 2010 of a new £50 million brick factory at Measham, operated by Hanson Building Products. The new factory can produce 30 000 bricks per hour and at the time of opening it was the most modern of its type in Europe. Measham has more than 6 million tonnes of clay reserves, sufficient to last for 25 years at the current production level of 100 million bricks per year.

The other main producer in The National Forest is Ibstock Brick, a company that was established in 1825 for mining operations. By the 1830s the mining site was producing supplies of clays suitable for making bricks. Over the next ten years, a primitive brickworks was developed. This sideline grew due to mechanisation and assumed a greater importance at the beginning of the twentieth century. In 1928 the coal pits closed and the company's sidelines of brick-, tile-, and pipemaking were elevated to centre stage. Ibstock Collieries changed its name to Ibstock Brick & Tile Company in 1935. It is now the largest brick manufacturer in the UK

with an annual capacity of more than 900 million bricks.

LIME

Limemaking was only a small-scale industry in The National Forest because of the very limited supplies of *limestone*. Records show that quarrying for lime at Ticknall (Walk 10) began as early as 1393 and continued to 1950. Limestone in the Ticknall area was also worked for building stone, mortar and fertiliser for soil. To produce mortar, an early cement for building, the limestone was stacked in kilns in layers with coal and set alight to produce quicklime, which was then mixed with sand and water. This process at Ticknall may well extend back into Roman times; indeed, it is thought that the Romans

Western entrance of the Ticknall tramway tunnel going into the former limeworks.

Painting of the former quarry at Dimminsdale in the Ticknall Limestone.

Photograph © Leicestershire County Council Museums Service

developed this process. The process of 'marling' the land, or the spreading of lime, dates back to medieval times when fields were only used once every three years due to lack of fertility. Any unburned limestone was used to build houses and walls.

The lime yards expanded in the 17th century and again in the 18th century, when caves were excavated into the rock faces. The lime was mainly used locally but transport networks developed to export it farther afield with the Ticknall Tramway, opened in 1802, linking the pits to the Ashby Canal. New markets were found and the lime-burning expanded. The coal needed was brought from local pits. Although the

tramway has now been removed, its course can still be seen, as embankments and cuttings to the south of Ticknall (Walk 10). A tunnel in the grounds of Calke Abbey still remains and is a scheduled monument.

The first kiln was built around 1804, providing lime for mortar in the construction of Moira Furnace. Soon after, six additional kilns were built and a separate limeworks established, although the limeworks had ceased production by 1850.

When abandoned, the caves formed popular picnic spots with the local inhabitants, but this practice ceased in 1952 with the collapse of a cave. The caves can be seen in the extreme south eastern part of the former workings and evidence of cave collapse is apparent within the main part of the limeyards (Walk 10). The decline of the Ticknall limeyard was caused by the failure to use new technology and the coming of the railways. This made limestone in the Peak District much more accessible.

There is little written of the limeworkings at Dimminsdale. Principally, the mining and burning of lime started in the 13th century and continued through to the latter part of the 19th century. Between 1830 and 1891, the quarries were served by a branch of the Ticknall Tramway.

Lime production at Grace Dieu dates back to the medieval period. The nunnery was selling lime from around 1414. Coal from nearby at Coleorton and Swannington probably provided fuel for the process. The exact date of closure is not known but was probably in the first part of the 19th century. An 1836 map still marks the limeworks, but it is not marked on the 1885 OS map.

Cave formed by limestone mining at Ticknall.

BUILDING STONES

Good building stones are only found in three areas of The National Forest. The best quality building stones come from Charnwood Forest. Commonly, buildings are constructed from a variety of rocks, resulting in a diversity of colours and an attractive appearance. These stones had been in demand since Neolithic times, but the first evidence of use for building was by the Romans. In 1235, Grace Dieu Priory was built from Whitwick stone. Other notable buildings include Mount St Bernard Abbey, built in the 19th century and, more recently, the Blackbrook Reservoir dam. The Charnwood stone was generally used as rubble stone so there are rarely any hand cut or sawn blocks. Another Charnwood stone, from just outside The National Forest, is the Mountsorrel granodiorite. This has been used for the construction of local buildings, walls (Walk 4) and paving stones.

The other main building stone resource in The National Forest area is the Bromsgrove Sandstone, which is best seen in many of the churches dating from the 12th and 13th centuries. Bromsgrove Sandstone was also used for the construction of Ashby Castle (p.34). The *sandstone* used varies from reddish brown to 'white' (pale greenish grey to buff) in colour and individual buildings are often composed of a mixture of the two. Bromsgrove Sandstone was sometimes supplemented with Carboniferous sandstones from the local coalfields, for example the church in Walton-on-Trent. Occasionally, Carboniferous sandstone was the sole building stone, for example at Dunstall church.

Other stones that have been used very locally for building in The National Forest are the Millstone Grit sandstone,

Wall of Charnian building stone showing the wide variety of block sizes used.

Houses in Quorn built in Charnian stone with Swithland slate roofs.

which was used quite extensively in the Melbourne area, and Carboniferous *limestone*, quarried from Grace Dieu and other outcrops.

ARCHAEOLOGY

Any account of the archaeology of an area can only ever be a snapshot of a developing picture. Evidence continues to accumulate from fieldwork by professional and amateur archaeologists and our picture of the The National Forest area has been transformed over the last 30 years.

Prehistory

Tuffs from Charnwood Forest may have been exploited 500 000 years ago for hand-axe production, but the earliest known site is an Upper Palaeolithic (about 10 000 BC) hunting stand discovered in

The church at Weston-on-Trent. This is built mainly of Bromsgrove Sandstone, with some Carboniferous sandstone.

Breedon Brooch.

Bradgate Park. The northern fringes of Charnwood show scatters of Mesolithic (8500–4500 BC) flint tools at Grace Dieu and Charnwood Lodge, probably repre-senting hunter-gatherer camp sites. Flint finds of unknown age have been recov-ered from around Shepshed, Coalville and Ibstock. There was considerable activity in the area in Neolithic (4500–2200 BC) and Early Bronze Age (2200–700 BC) periods. Charnian stone axes (the Charnwood Axe industry) are known, with a concentra-tion west of Blackbrook Reservoir. Early Bronze Age axe heads are known from Bardon Hill and burials are known from Mount St Bernard Abbey. In the glacial sands and gravels between Heather and Swepstone up to a dozen ring ditches, thought to be tombs or barrows of this period, have been recorded as well as a number of rectangular enclosures prob-ably dating from the Iron Age (700 BC–AD 43). A hill fort at Beacon Hill is also tentatively dated as late Bronze Age, yield-ing bronze tools. Iron Age hill forts on the edge of The National Forest at Breedon and Ratby were presumably important local centres. Cropmarks visible from the air indicate rectangular enclosures, and finds of stone grinding tools (quern stones) and pottery suggest many sites existed in the Bronze Age period, but only

a few have been excavated e.g. at Nor-manton le Heath and Botcheston.

Roman period

Two major Roman highways cross the forest. One, Ryknild Street, followed the line of the A38. The second, the Via Devana, ran from Leicester to Moira, continuing through Burton upon Trent, possibly to Chester. A Roman town lay on this highway between Ravenstone and Ibstock. The town produced pottery and tiles, and there is also evidence of a fort. Beveridge Lane, which runs east of this town, is probably also a Roman road. It may be a continuation of the Salt Way that crosses the River Soar at Barrow and clearly leads into Charnwood Forest. There is thought to be a north–south road running through The National Forest area linking the towns of Mancetter (Warwickshire) and Ratcliffe on Soar (Nottinghamshire). Close by this road, a rare high-status Roman villa was discovered at Ibstock. A site at Blackbrook Farm on the northern edge of The National Forest has also yielded considerable amounts of tile, suggesting a production

Photograph © Peter Liddle, courtesy of NFC

Excavation showing Roman kilns at Ravenstone, Leicestershire.

site here. The Romans quarried Swithland Slate from Swithland Wood and Groby in Charnwood Forest during the period AD 100–400, mainly for roofing purposes. Swithland Slate and various Charnian rocks were used as rubble building stone, while there is also evidence of a rural pottery industry at Groby, Markfield and Normanton le Heath.

Anglo-Saxon period

There is currently little evidence for early Saxon activity in The National Forest. Pottery of this age has been found at Swepstone and a complete pot recovered from Breedon Hill. The Breedon Hill site became important in the late 7th century, when a monastery was founded within the ramparts of the Iron Age hill fort and the carvings preserved in the present parish church are of national importance. An abbey was established at Burton upon Trent in 1002–1004. Close to The National Forest is the village of Repton. Formerly the headquarters of a Viking army, it became the burial place of the Saxon kings of Mercia. It was a major religious centre but Lichfield has a better claim to be the 'political' capital.

Late Saxon and medieval periods

Charnwood Forest was one of the least populated areas of Leicestershire but despite this, it was an important resource for grazing, hunting and the quarrying of slate and hard rocks. In the 12th and 13th centuries religious communities were created at Charley, Ulverscroft and Grace Dieu. Hunting parks were created at Bardon and Bradgate, and monastic granges at, for example, Hugglescote. To the west of Charnwood Forest, Bagworth was an important centre which had a castle by the 14th century. Other castles existed at Whitwick, Groby, Ravenstone

and Ashby, the latter a centre for the area. The Grey family created their own centres at Groby and later Bradgate, both of which, in part, survive. At a lower social level, Donington le Heath Manor House is a well-preserved example of a 13th century middle-class residence.

Around Oakthorpe, Donington le Heath and Swannington there is evidence of early coal mining. During excavation of the Lounge opencast site, archaeologists recorded galleries of mines dating to the 15th century and recovered clothing, shoes, candles and tools. Outcrops of *limestone* from Breedon down to Grace Dieu were also quarried for limemaking in the medieval period and later.

HISTORIC BUILDINGS

During and after the Norman Conquest, buildings of note were generally either defensive structures such as castles, or religious or monastic establishments. Norman castles were generally built of wood, so they soon decayed and no evidence remains of them today. However religious buildings were usually built of stone and, as a result, have lasted through the centuries.

Religious buildings

A Benedictine monastery was established at Burton upon Trent in 1002–1004 and a shrine to St Modwen (a 7th century nun) was constructed on an island in the River Trent. The abbey fell into disrepair and was plundered for stone following the dissolution of the monasteries in 1539; there are only a few remnants today. The 14th century moated manor house of Sinai Park, thought to have been a convalescent home for the monks, is apparently linked to the abbey via a subterranean passageway. It is a classic timber-framed, wattle-and-daub

Grace Dieu priory.

the Normans in the early 12th century) and Repton (re-established 1172); they are both just outside The National Forest, but owned extensive tracts of land within the Forest. Today only the chancel survives from the priory at Breedon, and serves as the parish church. All that remains of the priory at Repton is the original guest house, now transformed into the school. The Cistercian abbey of Mount St Bernard is a relative newcomer to Charnwood Forest, established in the 1830s. The abbey was designed by the celebrated Augustus Pugin. It was not actually completed until 1939, the monks supplying much of the labour.

Many churches in The National Forest have medieval origins or earlier. An example is St Michael and St Mary in Melbourne (Walk 3) with an ornate 12th century interior. Other churches of note include that on the Staunton Harold estate

construction. The house was badly neglected after the Second World War and nearing collapse, but is now being carefully restored to its 16th century appearance. In the 13th century, the Cluniac Monks of Bermondsey also built a tiny religious house at Alderman's Haw, in Charnwood Forest.

The ruined Augustinian priory of St Mary, established at Ulverscroft in 1134, is the best-preserved example of this type of monastery in The National Forest. A priory was also established at Grace Dieu in 1240. This monastery also fell into disrepair after the dissolution of the monasteries, and is now a ruin apparently haunted by the spectre of a nun wearing a white habit, known as the 'White Lady'. Other monasteries in the Forest disappeared completely.

Augustinian priories were also established at Breedon on the Hill (p.56) (rebuilt by

Photograph © Robert Morris, courtesy of NFC

One of the Saxon carvings in Breedon Church.

Ashby Castle. Note the thick wall built of rubble stone, with the smooth facing sandstone.

(Walk 10), founded by Sir Robert Shirley in 1653, and the beautiful Victorian church of Holy Angels at Hoar Cross, Yoxall. Many of the 12th and 13th century churches were rebuilt in the 19th century.

Castles and fortified manor houses

The ancient castle at Whitwick has origins in the 11th century, whilst Groby Castle had links with late Anglo-Saxon England and later become a medieval garden, the remains of which survive to this day. Ashby-de-la-Zouch Castle was also a fortified manor house, originally built in the 1160s. If you visit the remains of Ashby Castle, you will see good sections through some of the walls that show a thin outer facing of Bromsgrove Sandstone, and a thick interior of rubble stone. This is mainly Bromsgrove Sandstone but also includes some pieces of Charnian rocks. Bagworth Castle was another fortified moated manor house, probably built during the 14th century.

Fortified manor houses were built after the Norman Conquest. Donington le Heath manor house, near Coalville, was one such dwelling, built from local Charnwood stone in the 1290s. From 1670 the house was tenanted, and remained unchanged for three centuries; it deteriorated badly in the 1960s and was rescued from dereliction by Leicestershire County Council in 1965. Donington le Heath now functions as a museum.

Country houses

Wealthy landowning families, often of Norman descent, commonly built grand country houses in what was to become The National Forest. The Beaumont family acquired the manor of Overton (now Coleorton) in 1428, and built three successive houses, the last of which, Coleorton Hall, was constructed in 1807. The Ferrers family are associated with Staunton Harold Hall, which they obtained in the late 11th century. A succession of houses existed on the site; the current Palladian-style house was built by the 5th Lord Ferrers in the 1760s and is considered to be one of the finest country houses in Leicestershire.

Calke Abbey.

One of the most famous great houses in the Forest is Bradgate House, situated in Bradgate Park and once home to the ill-fated Lady Jane Grey. The house was constructed by Thomas Grey between 1499 and 1520 and was unusually built of brick manufactured from red clay quarried from nearby Triassic Mercia Mudstone. Lady Jane Grey was born at Bradgate in 1537, and spent much of her short life there. Following the death of her cousin Edward VI she was proclaimed Queen of England, only to lose the crown nine days later. She was tragically executed for treason by Mary Tudor on 12th February 1554. The house was unoccupied by 1720, in ruins by 1790, and has changed little over the centuries.

Calke Abbey, one of the most distinguished country houses in The National Forest, is associated with the Harpur Crewe family, who acquired it in 1622. Over the period 1701 to 1704, they turned the original Elizabethan courtyard house into the Baroque mansion that exists today. A 12th century Augustinian priory once stood on the site, but despite this, the house was renamed 'Calke Abbey' in 1808. It has changed little since the 1880s and was taken over by the National Trust in 1985.

The manor of Catton was bought by the Horton family in 1405. The current house dates from 1742 to 1745 and remains virtually unchanged today. However, many grand houses have sadly disappeared, particularly in the years after the Second World War. Casualties include Drakelow Hall, one-time home of the Gresley family, and Byrkley Lodge, once owned by the Bass family of brewing fame, who also owned Rangemore Hall which still survives today.

BREWERY INDUSTRY

Burton upon Trent has been closely linked with the brewing industry for centuries, as

Steam cooperage at Bass Brewery, Burton upon Trent and Breweries in Burton upon Trent from the River Trent.

Photographs © The National Brewery Centre Archive

the local water from wells was particularly well suited for the brewing of ales. The monks of Burton Abbey (p.32) were probably the first to recognise this: they collected water from wells in the Trent Washlands to brew their own beer. In those days water was not safe to drink, so ale was brewed in huge quantities for daily consumption by all. Inns were built to house travellers visiting the Abbey and its shrine to St Modwen. After the dissolution of the Monasteries in 1539, local inns continued to produce beer on a small scale.

But why was the water so well suited to brewing ale? The answer lies in its chemistry, which in turn is due to the geology of the area. It naturally contains a high level of gypsum in solution, derived from the rocks beneath Burton. The high sulphate content brought out the flavour of hops in the beer and the distinctive sulphurous aroma of Burton beer earned it the quirky nickname of 'Burton Snatch'. The high sulphate content also enabled more hops (a natural preservative) to be incorporated into the beer, increasing its shelf-life. Incidentally, brewers elsewhere in England today replicate this process, known as Burtonisation, by adding gypsum to the water used for brewing.

Commercial beer production began in Burton in the late 17th century when local tavern owners started to sell their beer farther afield. Beer was transported to London where it attracted the attention of shrewd businessmen. One, Benjamin Printon, moved to Burton in 1708 to open the first commercial brewhouse. Burton's brewing industry was further helped by the opening of the Trent Navigation Company in 1712 allowing the shipping of beer to Hull and then by sea to London, Europe, the Baltic Sea and Russia. This led to the evolution of Burton as a major town for brewing and exporting beer.

Subsequently, many brewers established themselves in Burton in the mid 18th century, the most notable being William Worthington (1744) and William Bass (who bought Worthington's brewhouse in 1777). By 1830, the Bass brewery had grown to be the largest in the world, employing more than 2500 people and by the late 1880s, producing almost one million barrels per year.

Problems with the overseas market in the early 19th century terminated this profitable market for Burton beer.

However, a new market was found in India, initially supplied by London-brewed beer. In 1822, Burton-based Samuel Allsopp successfully produced a hoppier-tasting version of the beer, thanks again to the sulphate-rich local water, and supplied the Indian market. Allsopp's beer became very popular and other brewers quickly followed suit. By 1888 Burton had 31 breweries, turning out three million barrels of beer a year at the height of production. This heralded the beginning of a golden age of brewing for Burton; at its peak, one quarter of all beer sold in Britain was produced there.

At the beginning of the 20th century, another slump in overseas beer sales caused many breweries to fail, and the First World War imposed a decline, due to shortage of labour and grain supplies. This time, no new markets were found and the number of breweries shrank from 20 in 1900 to eight in 1928. Despite this, during the Second World War Burton beer was still popular enough to spawn the euphemism 'gone for a Burton' (RAF pilots used this black humour when a comrade was killed or went missing in action; they had not died, they had simply nipped out for a pint of Burton beer). Today brewing remains an important industry in the town, and is currently home to six breweries. A small brewery also exists in Woodville near Swadlincote.

BIODIVERSITY AND LANDSCAPE

The biodiversity of The National Forest reflects its varied landscapes, their history and their underlying geology. Within the Forest, there are six main landscape 'zones' which each have characteristic mixes of habitats and wildlife. The best way to appreciate this is to visit each one in turn.

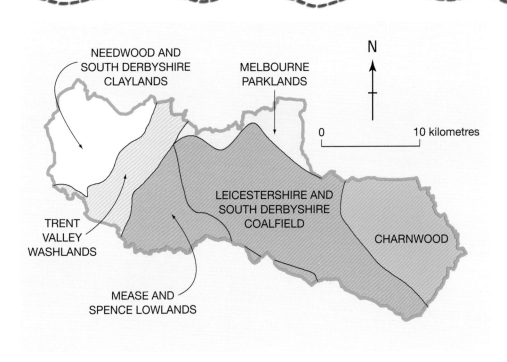

Landscape character areas of The National Forest.

Bluebells at Burroughs Wood near Ratby, Leicestershire, a Woodland Trust site in The National Forest.

Trent valley (Walk 8)

The Trent is one of England's great rivers and, over the millennia, its passage across The National Forest has carved out a wide valley with a distinct collection of habitats and wildlife. Despite intensive development pressures, its wide *floodplain* still contains fragments of open grassland and wet woodland. Elsewhere, decades of sand and gravel extraction have left a string of large lagoons, many of which are now oases for wildfowl, otters and water voles. At Croxall Lakes, the bank of the Trent has been remodelled and pulled back to create pools, riffles and islands. The result has been to reintroduce the natural processes of erosion and deposition that would, historically, have occurred along the length of the river.

Tatenhill village.

Needwood and the South Derbyshire claylands

The key characteristics of this landscape are a rolling plateau capped by glacial till, and prominent wooded heights west of the Trent with frequent plantations and ancient woodland. A manorial hunting ground of the Duchy of Lancaster until about 1366, it is now a sparsely populated mosaic of woodland, pasture, old parkland and arable farmland. The hedgerow pattern is generally subrectangular and the fields predominantly pasture but with some areas of more open arable farming. Hidden away in this landscape are real gems such as Brankley Covert, where ancient woodland and wood pasture (similar to parkland) are being expanded across former arable fields; or Yoxall Lodge, which

is carpeted with bluebells each Spring. The woodlands at Jackson's Bank, part of the Duchy of Lancaster's estate, retain much of their seminatural flora, such as bluebell, wood anemone, wild garlic, early purple orchid, herb Paris and wood spurge. East of the village of Tatenhill, a wooded scarp marks the edge of the Needwood Forest, from which the land falls dramatically away to the Trent Valley. There are red brick and half timber villages with *sandstone* churches. The road pattern is varied, linking a scattered settlement of villages and hamlets.

Lowlands of the rivers Mease and Sence (Walk 1)

Flowing west to the Trent, the River Mease forms the southern boundary of The

Lount Nature Reserve — formerly Lount Colliery.

National Forest. The key characteristics of the Mease and Sence lowlands are gently rolling landforms of low, rounded hills and valleys with flat land along river valleys, and a well-managed agricultural landscape. The Mease is internationally important for its wildlife; key species including spined loach, bullhead, white-clawed crayfish and otters. Between the Mease and the Trent, there is a low-lying swathe of rich farmland with hay meadows full of wild flowers and woodland copses that are home to a range of animals. This combination of habitats means that the area supports a great selection of woodland and farmland birds. Farm ponds provide refuges for dragonflies and amphibians. There are extensive, very open areas of arable cultivation and a strongly rectilinear hedge pattern of late enclosure, often dominating an open landscape. There are some deserted settlements and ridge and furrow, the latter possibly dating back to the immediate post-Roman period in the late 5th century. Tree cover is generally sparse and confined to copses and spinneys, with intermittent hedgerow trees and parks. Small red-brick villages often occur on hilltop sites and with prominent church spires.

The coalfield (Walks 1, 2, 7, 9 and 10)

Forming the core of The National Forest, the coalfield is its most populated landscape and probably the most altered by human activity dating back to the Industrial Revolution. As long ago as the 13th century coal has been mined from this area and, by the 20th century, the extraction of coal and clay had completely changed the landscape. The key characteristics of the coalfield are prominent coal tips, derelict land, clay pits, opencast coal workings and sprawling mining towns and villages. It is in this area that the creation of The

National Forest has led to the most visible transformation. Where once coal was king, spoil tips have been 'greened' with trees and now support a wide range of birds. Colliery yards are now grasslands filled with flowers, and what were once massive opencast mines are now some of the best sites for wildlife in the area. Even former sewage works have been transformed into nature reserves. The area has a gently-undulating landform of shallow valleys and ridges dominated by mainly low, thin hedges with few hedgerow trees, small woodlands and an increasing number of new woodlands. It is an open and rolling agricultural landscape of mixed arable and pasture farming, with areas of small fields, dense hedgerows and prominent groups of red brick miners' cottages. There are many industrial archaeological features of interest for surface and underground coal workings, together with cottages, tramways, the Ashby Canal and Moira Furnace.

Melbourne parklands (Walks 3, 6 and 10)

Extending north from the coalfield towards Derby, the Melbourne parklands roll down to the Trent. The area's key characteristics are steeply undulating landforms dominated by sandstone ridges, plateau tops with good views and large landscape parks with grand country houses, such as Calke Abbey. Characterised by large plantation woodlands, wide open fields, former market gardens and historic estates, the area is dominated by two reservoirs, Foremark and Staunton Harold. Foremark Reservoir is popular with wildfowl and other birds. At its southern tip lies Carver's Rocks, an SSSI for its ecological importance, which includes one of the last remnants of lowland heathland in Derbyshire. Nearby, the Calke Abbey estate contains nationally important parkland with spectacular ancient trees, some of which are thought to be almost 1000 years old. The estate also includes a series of ponds that are home to the threatened white-clawed crayfish. There are also grasslands grazed by a large herd of deer and an area of former *limestone* workings supporting lime-loving species which only occur in this part of the Forest. There is localised quarrying for a variety of products and imposing and dramatically sited churches, such as at Breedon on the Hill (Walk 3).

Rolling landscape of the Melbourne parklands.

Charnwood Forest (Walk 4)

At the eastern end of The National Forest lies Charnwood Forest, a hunting forest in the early 12th century. Charnwood is a unique upland landscape that is dominated by its geology, rising out of a lowland farming area. Rocky outcrops are common and the underlying volcanic and granitic rocks create ideal conditions for open heathland, bracken and acid grasslands. These are interspersed with *mudstone* vales of pasture fields. The increase in grazing in the 16th century meant that much of the original woodland was cleared to create Charnwood Forest as it exists today: a mosaic of ancient woodlands, species-rich meadows and heathland, with dry stone walls and hedges. The result is the richest assemblage of wildlife within The National Forest. Nature reserves such as Ulverscroft and Lea Meadows showcase grasslands full of wild flowers; ancient woodlands provide shelter for a range of plants and animals, and open heathland such as Charnwood Lodge provides some of the last 'wilderness' in the Forest. There are also a number of SSSIs for both their geological and biodiversity interests. The Forest itself has attractive villages and scattered farmsteads at its centre, with the large settlements of Leicester, Loughborough and Coalville at the edge. There is a strongly rectilinear pattern of parliamentary enclosure fields and roads, and attractive historic parks such as Bradgate Park. The village buildings are dominated by dark Charnwood stone. Also dominating the landscape are reservoirs and man's influence in the shape of the quarrying (aggregates) industry. Currently two working quarries operate in The National Forest but numerous abandoned ones provide havens for wildlife.

WALKS

Most walks can be completed in half a day although some include the chance to visit other attractions that would extend the walk into a whole day. All of the walks are unsuitable for disabled people apart from the building stones walk in Burton upon Trent.

KEY TO WALK MAPS

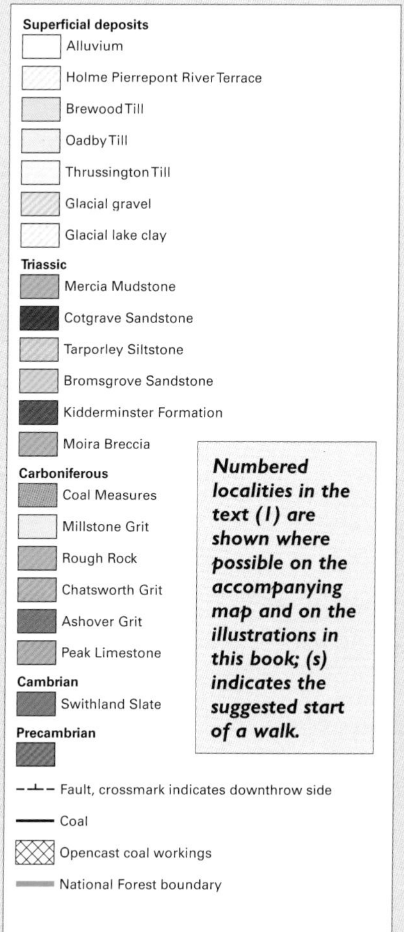

Superficial deposits
- Alluvium
- Holme Pierrepont River Terrace
- Brewood Till
- Oadby Till
- Thrussington Till
- Glacial gravel
- Glacial lake clay

Triassic
- Mercia Mudstone
- Cotgrave Sandstone
- Tarporley Siltstone
- Bromsgrove Sandstone
- Kidderminster Formation
- Moira Breccia

Carboniferous
- Coal Measures
- Millstone Grit
- Rough Rock
- Chatsworth Grit
- Ashover Grit
- Peak Limestone

Cambrian
- Swithland Slate

Precambrian

Numbered localities in the text (1) are shown where possible on the accompanying map and on the illustrations in this book; (s) indicates the suggested start of a walk.

–·–·– Fault, crossmark indicates downthrow side

—— Coal

▨ Opencast coal workings

▬ National Forest boundary

Key to the walk map

Walk 1

A walk from The National Forest Waterside Centre to Acresford

An ancient Triassic river, important aquifers and the coal-mining heritage

Distance: about 9.5 km (6 miles)
Time: 2.5 hours

Park at **Conkers Waterside Centre, Bath Yard, Moira [1]** and check the closure time of the car park. Walk back to the road, turn left and after about 100 m take the footpath on the right. Cross a field, go under the former railway bridge and stop for a moment to read the interpretation board detailing the history of **Barrett Pool Woodland**. The stretch of woodland is very short and you will soon come out into the grounds of a house. There is a pond on your left that can display a diverse range of bird life, and the house is on your right. Go round the entrance gate and out on to a road, turn right, and head along the paved road into

Face of old quarry in the Kidderminster Formation at Acresford, showing sandstone, pebble sandstone and conglomerate. The face is about 8 m high.

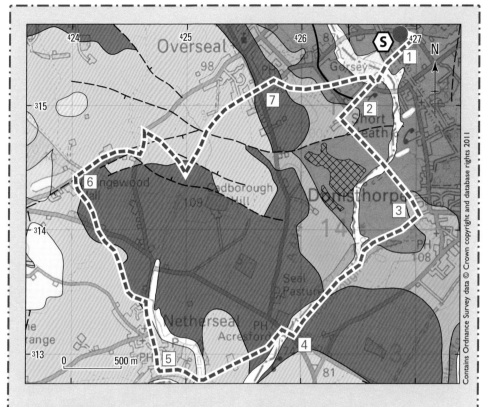

Short Heath. [2] Follow the road until you reach a sharp right-hand bend and then take the track straight ahead; after about 100 m, at **Shortheath Farm**, take the footpath on the left. This path is not clearly marked, so you will need to look out for the waymarker in the hedge.

Proceed down the hill and straight ahead through a gate in the middle of the next fence. The path looks as if it turns to the left here but you should turn slightly to your right and climb over a gate — there is no stile so take care. Proceed down the right-hand side of the hedge and across three fields to a stile, cross the bridge over

Hooborough Brook and enter **Lockharts Wood**, a National Forest Tender Scheme site. An interpretation board provides details relating to the woodland. In the autumn you will be able to admire the colourful feature trees planted here, such as the beautiful red and scarlet oak, tulip trees and the rare wild service tree.

Go up the other side of the valley, on to a track and up on to a ridge just before some houses, following the waymarkers. Continue along the track, passing a waymarker on the left. At the end of the track, cross the end of a cul de sac passing houses and enter into the field **[3]**. Here, take the footpath to the right, heading back downhill again. Crossing the field, head for the next waymarker and take the second footpath on your left, over a stile. Follow the path to the right alongside the woodland, and at the waymarker, follow the path into the woodland, down some steps. Shortly, you will come to a second flight of steps after which you will proceed along the river valley on a raised embankment. When you are out of the woodland, look out for the *sandstone* cliff just to the left of the main path and an interpretation board which explains the geology of the area. This area used to be a large pit extracting sand and gravel (as sandstone and conglomerate) from the Kidderminster

Formation of the Sherwood Sandstone Group.

The footpath emerges at houses in **Coopers Close** in the small village of **Acresford [4]**. Turn right here and walk along the A444 for a short distance then take a left turn at the **Cricketts Inn** and follow the paved road for a kilometre to **Netherseal**. In Netherseal, stop and look at **St Peter's Church [5]**. This was built of Triassic Bromsgrove Sandstone in the 19th century but it actually stands on the site of a former 13th century church. Several of the features of the earlier church remain including the tower and some of the monuments inside. However, it may not be possible

Wall in Netherseal built on an outcrop of Bromsgrove Sandstone.

to go into the church as it tends to be locked. Sir Nigel Gresley, the engineer who designed the locomotive Mallard, is buried in the church cemetery. Just beyond the church at the bend in the road on your right, there are small outcrops of the Bromsgrove Sandstone Formation showing *cross-bedding* (pp.8 and 10). This is the youngest unit of the Sherwood Sandstone. Netherseal was more famous for its coal mining and had a large colliery with two shafts which were sunk in 1867. Five hundred workers were employed in the 19th century to extract coal from the Main, Stockings and Eureka seams. Netherseal has two pubs and a post office shop so you may want to stop for refreshment.

Walk through the village. Many of the place names in this area have the word 'Seal' which suggests the area was once heavily forested. Nether means 'lower' and Over (of the neighbouring village Overseal), means 'upper'. At the end of the village, take the footpath just after the Sports Club on the left. At the far end of the sports field, climb up into the adjacent field and proceed along the next hedge. At the bend in the fence, veer to the right and cross two fields. The path is vaguely marked here and the fields may contain planted crops, so it may be necessary to deviate around the edges in summer. Exit the second field at the gap in the fence marked by a footpath sign, cross the road and take the path that goes across a field close to **Grangewood Hall [6]**. The path does a right then left turn, passing a pond on your left and continue on

to a road. Turn right here and you will be roughly following the line of the Gunby Lea Fault which fractures the Coal Measures of the South Derbyshire Coalfield.

Unfortunately, there is no path along this road but there is a good grass verge on the left hand side and a partial verge on the right; the road is not busy. At the T junction, turn left on to a busier road and again you can walk on grass verges. After about 50 m, just before the next bend in the road, go over the stile to your right and enter **Gunby Lea and Broomfield's Wood**. Take the track on the left which skirts round the left edge of the woodland. After about 500 m cross through the hedge and follow the track up across four pasture fields towards **Overseal**. Follow the minor road through houses up to the main A444, cross over the road in **Overseal [7]**, on to Moira Road and take the footpath on the right after 150 m. The path goes to the right of a white house between gardens. At the end of the path, cross the stile and carry straight on and through a farm gate keeping the farm buildings to your left. The path then goes over a field and heads approximately due east (about 45° to the farm buildings) to where the hedge juts out ahead of you. Cross a stile and head down the next field across another stile and on to the road. Cross the road and then head diagonally across the next two fields emerging at **Short Heath**. Turn left and take the footpath back towards the **Conkers Waterside Centre**.

Walk 2

Black gold at the heart of The National Forest

An illustrious mining heritage: a legacy of deep collieries, opencast sites, mining subsidence and an elusive new species of rabbit!

Distance: approximately 12 km (7.4 miles)
Time: about 4 hours

Park at Conkers Waterside Centre, off the B5003, on Bath Yard, Moira. Check the closure time of the car park before setting off on your walk.

This circular walk will take you on a journey through the industrial heart of

Photograph © Charlie James, courtesy of NFC

The 'Conkachoo' train connects the Conkers Waterside to the Discovery Visitor Centre.

The National Forest, past former coal mines and opencast sites, to explore aspects of the South Derbyshire Coalfield. In the 19th century, coal was vital to the commercial development

Photograph © UK Coal

Hicks Lodge opencast site.

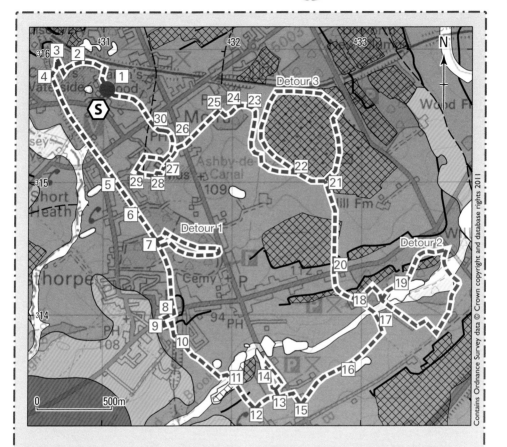

of the region and it shaped both the landscape and the livelihood of the local communities. Walking here today, many people would not realise the past history of the area as the landscape has been changed beyond recognition, first by coal mining, then opencast working and finally by restoration as part of the developing National Forest. As a result, there is little to see today of the Carboniferous Coal Measures rocks that formed the basis of this industry.

The walk begins at Conkers Waterside **[1]** the visitor attraction at the heart of The National Forest. Conkers consists of the Discovery and Waterside visitor centres, linked by a small train ('Conkachoo'). The Waterside visitor centre is built on the site of the old Bath Pits (opened 1813) whilst the Discovery centre is situated at the former Rawdon Colliery (opened 1821). When Bath Pit closed, saw mills and a dry dock for the repair of boats and barges were constructed, and steam locomotives were repaired on the site. On closure, the site was cleared and the area developed as part of the Conkers Waterside visitor centre and National Forest Company offices. How different the scene must look today.

Walk along the tarmac footpath to the right-hand side of the adventure playground. Turn left to cross the Conkachoo line before the bridge, signposted Ashby Woulds Heritage Trail (be aware that the gates will close if a train is coming). Immediately on your right-hand side is a large granite marker advertising the 'Ennstone Trail' (note the large white crystals of *feldspar*, clear glassy *quartz* and shiny black mica). Walk downhill and pass under a brick bridge **[2]**, then turn left and follow the path past the granite picnic benches and into the woodland **[3]**. Bear left, following signs for the Ashby Woulds Heritage Trail and Measham. You can see evidence of past mining activities from clues in the landscape: glittering fragments of coal represent all that is left of the mine spoil after restoration. Hollows and depressions in the land surface may be due to mining subsidence, excavation of clay pits or dewatering of coal-washing and slurry ponds. Although it is not possible to see the underlying geology, you are now walking over the Pennine Middle Coal Measures of late Carboniferous age, about 310 million years old, which consist of alternating or interbedded *mudstone*, *siltstone*, *sandstone* and coal seams.

In a short distance you will reach a small pond **[4]**; there is a cafe on site if you would like to stop for refreshments. Another granite marker and interpretation board highlight the route of the Conkers Circuit

and provides more information on the area. Turn left towards Measham to join the Ashby Woulds Heritage Trail. You are now walking on an old dismantled railway track, the Ashby and Nuneaton Joint Railway that opened in 1871 to service the collieries in this area.

Ashby Woulds Heritage Trail, the line of an old railway track.

Walking along the trail you will notice an 'Ashby Canal Mine Seam' marker on your right which gives details of the depths to the coal seams beneath your feet; the Kilburn is the deepest at 353 m. Also notice the old railway signals a little farther along on the left. As you walk along the Ashby Woulds Trail, evidence of Coal Measures rocks can be seen in the soil, in the form of fragments of coal, mudstone and sandstone. Continue on the trail to point **[5]**, where brown signs point the way to the Ashby Canal and Moira Furnace (down a steep set of steps). You can cut the walk short here, by returning to Conkers Waterside via Moira Furnace and the canal.

Continue on the trail until you enter Donisthorpe Woodland Park [6]; a series of interpretation boards relate the history of the area.

As you enter the Woodland Park, you are walking over a small area of sandstone in the Pennine Middle Coal Measures. You can't see the rocks exposed at the surface as the area has been restored, but there are lots of fragments in the spoil around the park. After the pit closed, 300 000 cubic metres of colliery spoil were redistributed over the site to landscape the area. Since then, over 74 000 trees have been planted, comprising native oak, ash, poplar, grey alder and Corsican pine. If you have time, explore the trails around Donisthorpe Woodland Park, which has many paths that are accessible to disabled visitors (contact The National Forest Company for the 'Access for All' leaflet for this area). Otherwise, continue on the Ashby Woulds Trail, crossing a small bridge over a stream [7]. As the trail gently rises, keep straight on the main path towards the entrance gates of the park [8].

Leave the park and cross the road, turning right towards the church car park. If you have time, visit the church [9] and stop for a moment to examine its walls, which are built of Carboniferous sandstone. Evidence can be seen in the sandstone of graded bedding (coarse sand- to grit-sized grains that grade upwards into finer sand) and cross-bedding (pp.8 and 10). Cross back over the car park and walk downhill, following signs for the Ashby Woulds Trail. At the bottom of the

Meandering paths at Donisthorpe Woodland Park, created on the site of the former Donisthorpe Colliery, which closed in 1990.

hill bear left towards the houses [10], leaving the main trail, and notice the old brickyard chimney on your right. The mysterious tree rabbit, *Oryctolagus cuniculus arborealis*, has been allegedly sighted at several locations in the Donisthorpe area. This unique species is thought to have evolved from a single breeding pair of rabbits that burrowed into the local coal workings at the turn of the century. Within a few generations they had evolved black fur and a specialised retractable claw on their forelimbs which enabled them to cling on to vertical surfaces underground. They are also accused of gnawing the wooden pit props of older mines and damaging roof supports, which led to wide-scale subsidence on the surface. Eventually the rabbits left the mines for a new life on the surface, possibly due to mine closures, as the first sightings occurred after Oakthorpe Colliery closed. At risk again from predators, they used their retractable claws to climb and hide in trees and disused buildings. Since Donisthorpe Colliery closed in 1991, there has been a spate of sightings in the area, so keep your eyes open and have a closer look at the chimney. Whether this enigmatic creature really does exist is a matter of conjecture as there is no hard scientific evidence to support the phenomenon. However, local conservationists are keen to investigate this potential new species and many locals heartily believe in the rabbit's existence.

Continue downhill to cross a metal stile, entering a field. The path continues to the right of the pond in front of you. Saltersford Valley is immediately recognisable due to the large areas of open water known as 'flashes'. When coal was excavated, the ground gradually subsided causing the Saltersford Brook to flood the area. The valley was left derelict after the mines closed, but has since been improved and is now designated as a local nature reserve.

Follow the path and cross a small footbridge between the two ponds **[11]**. Continue uphill towards the houses, passing the Lowlands Farm Woodland on your right, a new woodland created through 'The National Forest Changing Landscapes Scheme' in 2009. Continue uphill and turn immediately left after a large metal gate **[12]**. Cross a stile into a field; the undulating ridge running east to west through the field marks the line of the former Ashby Canal. Although not visible, you are still walking over the sandstone-rich Pennine Middle Coal Measures. Continue on the path until you meet another footpath on the left **[13]**. If you have time, take a small

Reedbeds at 'Thortit Lake', Willesley Wood, another mining flash.

detour to the Saltersford Valley Picnic area **[14]**, a lovely place to explore and have a picnic. The 5.4 hectare (13 acre) site consists of woodland, mining flashes and meadows and has a rich variety of water birds. The native woodland is planted with oak, ash, cherry, hazel, guelder rose and dogwood and the wildflower-rich grassland areas are managed as traditional hay meadows. On the banks of the flashes there are fishing platforms suitable for disabled users and a wooden boardwalk gives access across part of the lake.

Return to point **[13]**, turn left and continue to the road; cross over and turn right to a footpath on the left, signed 'Willesley Wood ¾ mile' **[15]**. Follow the yellow footpath markers across two fields towards the barns of Lowlands Farm. Continue on the grassy path (which follows the towpath of the old Ashby Canal) past the farm buildings, and descend to the left-hand side of the lake **[16]**, another mining flash. You have now walked on to lower-lying ground of mudstone-rich Coal Measures that are softer and less resistant to erosion than the more resilient sandstone (behind you). The edge of the ridge crossing the field may be a *fault*, separating the two different rock types.

Walk past the lake and through the woodland until you cross a stile and enter a clearing. Take the path to the left into the Oakthorpe Picnic site, which stands on the remains of the former Oakthorpe Colliery.

After 100 m notice the hard-standing remains of the pit-head and two capped mine shafts on the right hand side **[17]** ('Oakthorpe No. 2, cap cast 21/02/91'). Continue on the path past the shafts. Follow the path past the picnic tables towards the car park, and then take the path on the right towards Willesley Wood **[18]**; an interpretation board provides lots of information about the site. Follow the path, bearing right downhill towards the lake **[19]** and look for evidence of Coal Measures rocks in the soil, which consists of mainly mining spoil. The lake is another mining flash that is quirkily known locally as the 'Thortit' Lake; it is only 1 m deep and stocked with carp, pike and tench. The lake formed in the early 1980s as underground mine workings collapsed causing subsidence. The woods are also known as Thortit Woods; apparently the pit heads were so well hidden in the woods that locals commented 'who'd a thought it'.

The Ticknall Tramway once crossed the site from Willesley crossroads (along the line of the present footpath) westwards to the Willesley Basin on the

Photograph © Annette McGrath, courtesy of NFC

Walking on one of the many paths through Willesley Wood.

former Ashby canal. If you have time, explore the woodlands and meadows around the site. Today Willesley Wood is owned and managed by the Woodland Trust and covers 56 hectares (138 acres) in total; it was one of the first new woodlands to be created in The National Forest in 1991, and is home to the rare native black poplar.

Retrace your steps back to the Oakthorpe car park, turning right up the main tarmac path; look out for signs of past mining activity in the woodlands here, in particular, a rusty metal track that could be the remains of the old tramway. Exit the main gate on to Ashby Road, cross the road with care, and then pass through the gate into Hick's Lodge [20]. Follow the bridleway north to the brow of a small hill and stop to admire the panoramic views over Hick's Lodge. Once an opencast site, it has been restored creating new woodland and ecological habitats including wetland areas and species-rich grassland.

Continue downhill towards the lake, where the path splits in two and take the path to the left [21]. In contrast to other water bodies seen on this walk, these lakes are not mining flashes; they are man-made features, dug out during restoration and landscaping of the opencast site in 2005/6. There are two islands on the main lake, created to provide nesting areas for ringed plovers and lapwings. If you have time, explore Hick's Lodge at your leisure — it is possible to complete a circular route around the site. The new National Forest Cycling Centre opened on this site in Spring 2011, complete with

visitor centre and cafe. Eight miles of safe, off-road, family-friendly trails and cycle paths have been created on the site.

After approx 300 m you will see a wooden footpath marker on your left. You will need to veer off to the left of the main path here [22] to follow more footpath markers, slightly downhill, towards another small lake (on your left). Continue to follow the footpath markers until you enter the woodland of Newfield Colliery [23] then follow a small overgrown path in a westerly direction through the trees. On first entering the woodland, look out for a ditch and a bank of earth crammed full of broken clay pipes, which are probably left over from previous clay-working at the colliery.

Photograph © Annette McGrath, courtesy of NFC

Section of the Ivanhoe Way long-distance footpath, as it enters the woodland of Newfield Colliery.

Continue on the path through the trees until you reach a large clearing — this represents a flattened area of mine spoil that has been left to naturally regenerate as heathland. Today, Newfield Colliery is typical of the habitat which can form naturally on restored colliery spoil. The site is a five hectare nature reserve, including areas of heathland, acid grassland, and oak/birch woodland. There are several small mining flashes, water-filled pits and pools in the woodlands that are rich in wildlife and plant life, including *Sphagnum* moss. Spend some time investigating the evocative and atmospheric woodlands at Newfield Colliery; elusive traces of its past industrial heritage are hidden in all corners of the woodland.

When you are ready, walk in a north-westerly direction parallel to the woodland edge, following the footpath markers towards a fence that marks the boundary of the site. Cross the stile [24] and walk along the field boundary (notice the capped mine shaft in the middle of the field) to a metal gate, marking another entrance to Newfield Colliery [25]. An interpretation board provides more information on the old colliery and yellow waymarker posts highlight the route of the Ivanhoe Way. Enter the woodland and continue on this leafy path through the trees for several hundred metres, following the yellow waymarker posts, until you meet the road. Turn right and after 50 m, cross the road and turn left [26] to follow the Ivanhoe Way towards the canal. The path continues beside the canal (notice the rusty remains of an old pumping engine on your left) towards Moira Furnace.

Turn right over the swing bridge and explore the area. The furnace is now a museum and heritage centre; a tearoom, craft units and toilets are nearby [27].

Return to the canal and turn right on to the towpath (sign-posted Donisthorpe) and walk past Moira Furnace. After approximately 150 m turn right through a metal gate and walk downhill on a path towards the limekilns [28]. Look closely at the limekilns — they are built with blocks of creamy-beige, medium-

View inside one of the old limekilns close to Moira Furnace and the Ashby Canal.

Photograph © Annette McGrath, courtesy of NFC

Photograph © Annette McGrath, courtesy of NFC

The rewatered Ashby Canal between Conkers Waterside Visitor Centre and Moira Furnace. Sarah's Wood can be seen on the far side of the canal.

to coarse-grained Carboniferous sandstone. Some of the blocks display well-defined horizontal bedding planes and graded beds, which consist of a layer of coarse grit that reduces in size (or 'fines') upwards to a fine-grained sand. You will also be able to pick out cross-bedding (pp.8 and 10) in the sandstone, defined by layers at a high angle to the bedding planes. Some of the sandstones are strongly coloured by secondary iron oxide minerals that were precipitated after the sediments accumulated.

Follow the path that leads directly away from the limekilns and canal and enter 'Pit Prop Wood' through a wooden gate [29] carved with its name. This lovely atmospheric old woodland is full of character, and invites you to explore further; follow the meandering leafy paths, cross the timber boardwalks and admire the unusual sculptures at leisure. Depressions in the woodland floor are all that remain of the former ironstone/clay pits that were excavated in this area. When ready, make your way back to the canal and Moira Furnace. Turn left onto the towpath, signposted towards 'Moira Lock, Conkers Waterside and Bath Yard Basin'. After about 300 m you will reach Moira Lock [30]. Cross the road with care and continue along the canal towpath until you reach your starting point near the canal basin at Conkers Waterside.

Walk 3

Breedon to Melbourne and Staunton Harold

Fossil landscapes, Triassic deserts and ice-age sediments, historic stone buildings and an attractive reservoir

Distance: about 13 km (8 miles)

This walk is generally unsuitable for the disabled although the part from Melbourne to Staunton Harold reservoir is suitable

This walks begins at the Priory Church of Saint Mary and Saint Hardulph, Breedon on the Hill [1], but an alternative starting point is at Staunton Harold Reservoir [9]. Parking is free at Breedon church but there may be a charge at Staunton Harold.

The Priory Church is a dominant and impressive feature in the landscape. It is visible for miles, perched on top of Breedon Hill and standing more than 120 m above the surrounding low ground. The hill is made of early Carboniferous *limestones*, in which the original calcite has been converted to dolomite. This *dolomitisation* process made the rock harder and thus more resistant to erosion.

The Priory Church has a lot of historical and geological interest, so you may wish to spend some time here. An excellent book detailing the

Breedon church and quarry from the air.

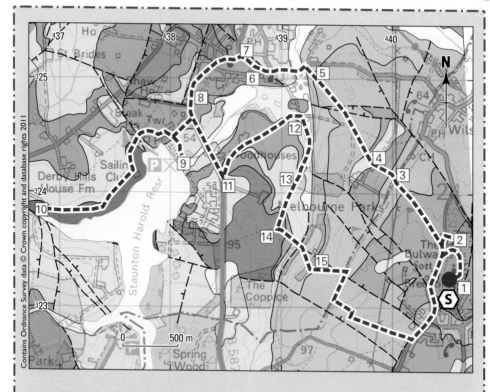

Contains Ordnance Survey data © Crown copyright and database rights 2011

history of the church is available to purchase inside. The site started as an Anglo-Saxon monastery around AD 676 (p.32), but the present church dates from the 12th century. Outside, in the churchyard, there are many headstones made of slate. There are two types: the local Swithland Slate (pp.5 and 22), displaying a rough back surface, and a Welsh slate, which is very smooth on both sides. The church itself is built of Triassic Bromsgrove Sandstone, from nearby quarries in the Trent valley or at Castle Donnington.

Inside Priory Church, there are two features of geological interest. There is a famous collection of Saxon carvings, seen in the walls; most are made from Jurassic rocks of the Lincolnshire Limestone, found 40 km away to the east of here. They were rescued from the Anglo-Saxon monastery when it fell into disrepair. Secondly, near the front of the church, carvings made from local alabaster can be seen. It was mined nearby at Aston and Chellaston.

Leave the church and walk back down the road you have just driven up. Around the first bend you will find a footpath on your right (there is no direction sign, just a post). Descend carefully down the first part of this path as it is steep and may be slippery when wet. Continue along the path, parallel to the road, and at the next yellow waymarker post turn right. You will then come to the viewing area that overlooks Breedon quarry **[2]**. There are two interpretation boards here that tell you about the geology and the quarry operations here.

Return to the main path, continuing back the way you have just come for about 100 m. Walk past the house and look for a footpath on your right on the other side of the road. Take this path and enter the golf course, taking care to look out for golfers and flying golf balls. The path is well marked by yellow posts; after a small rise and down the hill, there is a ditch on your left **[3]** in which you may be able to see some of the red clay from the Triassic *mudstone* bedrock. You can also see a good variety of trees, shrubs and wild flowers on this part of the walk. At the end of the golf course, cross a road and continue on up the hill. This next field is arable and if you look at the soil, you will see many pebbles **[4]**. They are mostly made of

quartz *(quartzites)* and flints that are derived from the extensive Anglian glacial deposits that once covered this area. A remnant of these glacial deposits (glacial till) caps the hill ahead. The quartzite pebbles are derived from older Triassic *conglomerates*. The flints are from chalk strata in Yorkshire and Lincolnshire; they tell us that the ice sheet that deposited them came down from the north-east.

Carry on over the hill and down the other side until you come to a track. Cross over the cattle grid and take a path that bears right across the next field. Notice here how scarce the pebbles are compared to the top of the hill. Continue across the next field **[5]** (look out for the mature lime trees) until you reach the road, then turn left and head into Melbourne. Note the stone wall on your left has been constructed from the local Millstone Grit *sandstones* which we are now crossing over. There are several examples of such walls throughout the town.

At the next crossroads, turn left and visit Melbourne Parish Church **[6]**. This fine church (dating from around AD 1120) and some of the surrounding buildings are also built of local Millstone Grit. In the walls, many of the stone blocks contain well-defined bedding surfaces, dipping quite steeply in some cases. This feature is known as *cross-bedding* (pp.8 and 10). Inside the church, some of the architecture is unique, which is why the church has been described as a 'cathedral in miniature'. There is a booklet available describing the history of the church. Another interesting building that is

Breedon quarry form the viewing area.

well-worth visiting is the 12th century Melbourne Hall and gardens. The hall is only open to the public in August (afternoons only), whereas the gardens are open from April to September. The hall is hidden from view behind the building facing the church.

Melbourne Hall and gardens.

Melbourne church.

Coming out of the church, go back to the crossroads and turn left towards Melbourne town centre **[7]**, passing the Methodist Church on your right (also built of the local sandstone). You might like to explore the town a bit more, find some refreshments and look at the famous Georgian architecture.

Starting from the monument in the town centre, bear left along the road and go up the hill, passing the United Reformed Church also built of local stone. Continue along the road, past the Melbourne Arms and hidden away on your left **[8]**, is one of the main quarries that supplied building stone

for the town. Go across the road signposted to Calke Abbey and take the next turning on the right to Staunton Harold reservoir and visitor centre **[9]**, where toilets, a refreshment kiosk and picnic areas can be found. The reservoir was created in 1964 with a capacity of 1400 million gallons, supplying water to around 800 homes and factories. It has a maximum depth of 25 m. If you explore the woods at the back of the visitor centre, you will see some outcrops of Millstone Grit sandstone. This particular *bed* is called the Rough Rock and represents the uppermost bed of sandstone in the Millstone Grit. If you look closely at the top surfaces of some of the outcrops you will see how coarse and gritty the sandstone can be.

The next part of the walk can be left out but is well worth it if you have time; allow about 45 minutes to complete it. This section of the walk is suitable for wheelchair users and an 'Access for All' leaflet is available from The National Forest Company. Go to the bottom corner of the car park, farthest away from the visitor centre and follow a path that will take you close to the

Centre of Melbourne with a typical Georgian building in the background.

northern shore of the reservoir, with wonderful views looking south across the water. This part of the walk has a wealth of flora and fauna with a wide variety of trees and shrubs, birds on the water, and a beautiful wild-flower meadow [10] created by Severn Trent

Northern end of Staunton Harold reservoir.

Water. You will pass an interpretation board along the way telling you about the meadows and some of the flowers that can be observed. In places, there are paths down to the waters edge.

At the end of the path [11], there is a barrier and another interpretation board that tells you about the tree-planting in the area. Turn around and head back to the visitor centre.

From the visitor centre, return to the main road and turn right. At the end of the pavement, there is a short stretch with no path before a footpath on the left signposted to Pool Farm [12]. Take great care on this stretch as the road can be very busy. Walk along the track to Pool Farm and at the entrance to the farm, take a right turn over a gate and into the field. The path is shown to go diagonally across the field but depending on the time of year and the crop, you may get diverted along the hedgerows. If you look at the soil in this field, you will see many blocks of sandstone, reflecting the Millstone Grit sandstone bedrock. At the far corner, go through into the next field and follow the path down a gentle slope, cross over a stile and head along the shore of The Pool [13]. This was originally the mill pond for the mill at Melbourne Hall. Again, you can see a range of bird life here and a good view across the water to Melbourne Parish Church.

At the end of The Pool, turn right along a track and then after 40 m, turn right again onto a footpath. This part of the walk runs along Carr Brook valley. Continue for about 1 km, crossing a small tributary valley. The short climb beyond the valley takes you up on to

Pond at Melbourne with the parish church in the distance.

the Pennine Coal Measures. These rocks contain the workable coal seams that fuelled the industrial revolution, but the small outcrops around Melbourne have never yielded any workable coals.

Approximately 150 m beyond the fence on your left at the top of the hill, you will come to a gate with a path signpost **[14]**. Follow the footpath going off to the left and proceed down the hill back into Carr Brook valley. Go through the woods in the valley bottom, then climb the steep escarpment on the other side. At the top of the next field turn right and about 40 m along the footpath turns left through the next woods. Be careful not to miss this as there is no signpost. The steep climb continues through the wood and over the Bromsgrove Sandstone Formation. These are the oldest Triassic rocks in this area and blocks can be

seen on the woodland floor. Beyond the woods, the climb continues onto the younger Tarporley Siltstone Formation which overlies the Bromsgrove Sandstone and forms the lowest part of the Mercia Mudstone Group. If you look at the soil in the field, you will see numerous small pieces of sandstone. In sunny weather, you will be able to clearly see grains of mica glistening in the rock. At the top of the hill, Breedon Church comes into view **[15]**.

At the bottom of the hill, turn right at the hedge and go back on to the golf course. Continue along the fairway and turn left by the teeing ground. The path then proceeds across the edge of the course until you reach the main road. Proceed towards the village and take a left fork as you reach Breedon. This will take you back to the church.

Walk 4

Broombriggs and Woodhouse Eaves

Explosive volcanoes and igneous intrusions

Distance: about 9.5 km (6 miles)
Time: about 3 hours

This walk can be very muddy when the weather is wet.

Park at Broombriggs Farm County Park **[1]** at SK524145; there is a pay and display machine at this car park. Take the track through a gate, alongside the line of oak trees and walk across the field uphill towards the woods. Continue along the track by the edge of a wood and note the diverse woodland with a wide range of tree species. Just before heading downhill there is a track up to the left to the top of Windmill Hill **[2]**. Here you can see the remains of a windmill that was last used in 1895 but still stood until it was burnt down in 1945. The rocks exposed here are *Tuffs* that were erupted from volcanoes centred around Bardon and Whitwick about 600 million years ago.

Follow the path back down to the main track and turn left **[3]**; note the many fragments of Charnian rocks on the track floor. The last part of the track is tarmacked before you reach

* *Note there are more walks in this part of Charnwood Forest in the companion publication 'Exploring the Landscape of Charnwood Forest and Mountsorrel'.*

Photograph © Gill Weightman, courtesy of NFC

Windmill at the top of Windmill Hill, Woodhouse Eaves.

the road which leads to the village of Woodhouse Eaves **[4]**. At the junction turn left down Maplewell Road. Notice the grey Swithland Slate rocks that make up the walls and roofs of the houses at the end of Mill Lane. Take a short detour and turn right at the bottom of Maplewell Road beyond the Pear Tree pub to see an example of an old Swithland Slate (pp.5 and 22) quarry next to the nursery building. The slates have been compressed and folded into a huge arch-shaped fold called an anticline. The rocks here dip steeply to the east and represent that particular side or limb of the fold.

Head back to the crossroads, turn right down Meadow Road and at the end by the primary school, turn through the gate on your right and take the right

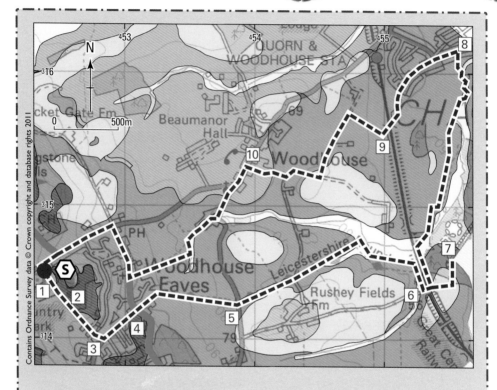

branching footpath across the fields on the Leicestershire Round. You are now on red Triassic clay but you may be able to see numerous fragments of Charnian rocks in the field. Cross over the road **[5]** and follow the yellow waymarks across several pasture fields along a valley, going over two farm roads. At the end of the field after the second of these roads, the footpath takes you over two stiles but you can miss these and head through the open gap in the hedge. As you crest a low rise ahead, you will see two waymarkers ahead of you. Make for the one to your right, following the well-trodden footpath. Ahead, you will see the tracks of the Great Central Railway. As you meet the railway line, bear left, cross over the bridge ahead and take the footpath immediately on your left **[6]**.

A small detour from the railway bridge can be taken along the road which leads down to Swithland Reservoir **[7]** and a quick look at the blocks in the dam wall reveals a different type of rock called *granodiorite*. This is an *intrusive igneous rock* that crystallised slowly at depth forming large crystals. The hill covered in trees beyond the reservoir at Mountsorrel hides the massive working Buddon Wood quarry which is one of the largest in Europe; the rock is extracted for buildings, roads and railway ballast, and was used to build the dam.

Charnian tuffs exposed at the top of Windmill Hill.

the next stile, then immediately left and you come to a tree-lined path. The footpath now follows the stream up to Mill Farm.

Follow the track into village of Quorn **[8]** and turn left along the road. Notice how the walls on your left are made up of the pink granodiorite from Mountsorrel and walls on the right are made up of mainly grey Charnian rocks. At the bend in the road, go left along Buddon Lane and at the end, take the footpath ahead, across a pasture field and into a tree-lined section which takes you past the edge of the Nature Conservation Area again. Go under the railway bridge **[9]** and then head up the hill. As you traverse up the hill you will first encounter Triassic clays and then pebbly glacial till towards the top of the hill — can you see any pebbles? Turn left at the junction along a track and road for about 750 m, then at the next junction, turn left towards the village of Woodhouse. Here again the

The main route now heads back along the opposite side of the railway track towards the village of Quorn. Follow the yellow waymarkers along the edge of a wood populated mainly by sycamore trees. The path leads away from the railway line, round a corner and over a stream into more mixed woodland. You can make out a pond to your right beyond the fence. Continue to follow the waymarkers, turning right then left and into a Nature Conservation Area. Turn right, over

Swithland Reservoir dam. Note the block of Mountsorrel granodiorite in the foreground.

buildings are made up of Swithland Slate and other Charnian stones. Turn left and at the next junction, **[10]** bear left into School Lane, past the Church of St Mary in the Elms. If you go into the churchyard, you will see that many of the gravestones here are made of Swithland Slate. These can be distinguished from the later Welsh slate by having rough, uneven backs compared to the smooth-surfaced Welsh slates.

Follow the road down past Pestilence Cottage, an unusual house built around 1300. There is a plaque outside the house telling you about its history. At the bend in the road turn right up School Lane and take the footpath straight on at the end of the lane, up alongside a stream. This path emerges alongside the playing fields at Woodhouse Eaves; turn right along the Main Street and then left at the Bulls Head; this will bring you back to the Broombriggs Car Park. You may like to stop for refreshments at the Bulls Head, or you can turn left and go into the main part of the village where there is another pub and shops.

Photograph © Gill Weightman, courtesy of NFC

Pestilence Cottage, Woodhouse.

Walk 5

Hanbury to Fauld crater

An ancient forest, glacial deposits and explosive gypsum works

Distance: approximately 9 km (5.5 miles)
Time: about 3 hours

This walk starts in the village of Hanbury, a small and pleasant village seven miles north-west of Burton upon Trent. The village overlooks the beautiful Dove valley and also has views north to the moorlands and hills of Derbyshire. The route straddles the boundary of The National Forest and takes you

through the northern extremity of the ancient Needwood Forest a chase or royal forest that today includes some of the UK's most ancient woodland. It is a relic of the forest which was granted to the first Earl of Lancaster in the 13th century and some areas are still in the ownership of the Duchy of Lancaster today. The forest was drastically reduced in the early 19th century, with large areas of chase and deer-park cleared to make way for farmland. The walk mainly crosses over the youngest sedimentary deposits from the last glacial period. However, very little can be seen of this glacial till (a mixture of clay, sand, gravel and boulders), as the area is extensively laid to pasture.

Fauld crater.

Photograph © Tony Waltham, courtesy of NFC

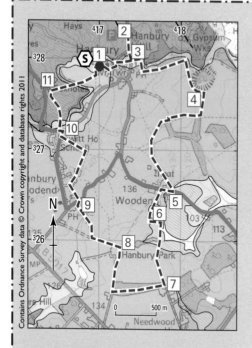

Proceed back along Church Lane and take the second road on the left. After about 50 m, take a footpath off to your right, through a garden and over a stile. Look over to your left and you will see magnificent views across the Dove valley. Head for the right-hand corner of the field, go over another stile and on to the road. If you park in one of the other car parks **[2, 3]** in the village, you will come up the hill along this road. Cross over the road and the footpath continues just a little way on your left. Go over another stile, cross a field and two more stiles. In the next field, you can appreciate more fabulous views over the Dove valley. Head to the right of the pylon in the far corner of the field by the woodland, go through a gate and you will see the next gate ahead on the far side of the field.

There are three places to park in the village (see map), the church **[1]** is probably the best place to park, but not on a Sunday morning as the car park is used by church-goers.

Start by visiting the St Werburgh's church on Church Lane, built of nearby Bromsgrove Sandstone (p.29). You can see evidence of *cross-bedding* (pp.8 and 10) in many of the stones. Look inside the church and admire the magnificent stained-glass window above the altar, the fine alabaster tombs, the Anglo-Saxon cross and colourful 19th century murals. Outside in the graveyard, there are some headstones made from the local Swithland Slate quarried in Charnwood Forest. These can be easily recognised by their rough back surfaces.

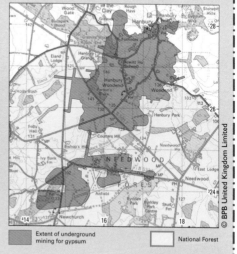

Gypsum workings associated with Fauld mine.

Contains Ordnance Survey data © Crown copyright and database rights 2011

Cross another stile back into woodland and after about 15 m, turn right through a gate. Follow this path, taking a left turn at the next junction, followed by a right turn that takes you along past the Fauld crater.

In places, you can see into the deep crater and note how extensively it has been colonised by woodland since it formed. The mine entrance lies just to the north of the crater and for much of this walk, you have been going over the underground caverns of the mine (p.66). Continue around the crater perimeter until you reach the memorial where you can read about the disaster [4] (p.16).

Carry on along this path, through a gate and take the next footpath off to the right. Another gate takes you into a pasture field. Follow the hedge line, through a third gate and then turn to the right at the next fence line. At the end of the field turn left, then after about 20 m turn right, cross a stile and take the footpath through a small copse. Crossing another stile into a pasture field, you will see houses to your right and farm buildings straight ahead. There is no footpath marked on the ground on this section of the walk. Head for the end of the hedge running into this field, go past this, turn left and go through a gate into another field. Again there is no clear path marked

Looking over the Dove valley.

here. Climb up on to the ridge ahead of you and head for the telegraph pole on your right and cross the fence; this is not an easy crossing so take care. Ahead of you, you will see a pair of telegraph poles to your right and a single pole to your left. Head for this and you will come to a waymarker by the next hedge. Here, take the path indicated off to your left — the path shown going straight on towards the farm buildings is no longer available. Go past the left hand side of the barn — this section can be very muddy in wet weather — then through two gates, on to the road and turn right **[5]**.

After a short walk along the road, there are two paths marked off to your left, either of which can be taken. The first of these involves negotiating a difficult fence and a very muddy area when wet. The second takes you through a garden and gate. When in this next field bear to the right, head for a short length of fencing jutting out into the field and go through the gate. The path is well marked from here, taking you around the edge of some new woodland **[6]**.

This new area of woodland has been created by the Duchy of Lancaster on a redundant gypsum mine site through the National Forest Company's 'Changing Landscapes Scheme'. The land here was affected by subsidence, caused by shallow gypsum mine workings, which caused a number of features known as 'crown holes' to form. These are roughly circular in shape with diameters of over six metres and depths of between two and

seven metres. So treacherous is this ground that it could not be farmed. Instead, the 13 acre site has been designed to enhance the landscape by increasing the area of woodland that typifies this part of The National Forest, and to also attract wildlife and re-establish native species. Work started on the site in the winter of 2009/10 and planting was completed in the winter of 2010/11. A mixture of trees such as oak, ash, and silver birch are part of the woodland design that incorporates owl boxes, bat boxes, bluebell planting and the sowing of wildflowers amongst the open areas. PLEASE NOTE that the presence of the subsidence holes means that access into the wood is not allowed, but you can skirt the edge on the public bridleway. There is a convenient bench at the corner of this field to take a rest.

Walk down to the next waymarker, turn right and head across the field to the left end of the hedge ahead. Go through the next gate and note the sign warning you of gypsum subsidence ahead. In spite of this warning, there has been very little subsidence associated with the Fauld mine, apart from the redundant gypsum mine you have just visited. Continue on the well-marked path across a field, a ditch bridge, through a hedge and on to the farm buildings ahead of you. Go towards these buildings and turn right just before the house **[7]** (the second of two tracks off to your right), entering woodland. Note the diverse woodland including sweet chestnuts in the autumn and a plentiful supply of holly for Christmas. Continue through the woodland until

Greaves Wood.

you emerge on to a road. Turn right here and you will come to Hanbury Park Farm buildings **[8]**. Hanbury Park is an ancient enclosure originating from the medieval Needwood Forest; it has eleven veteran oaks and around 20 other mature trees.

Pass through the buildings and turn to the left through the gate. Veer to the right, go through another gate and head towards the right-hand corner of this field. Cross the stile here and almost immediately turn right after the next hedge. Continue to another hedge and turn left, heading towards some houses in the distance. The path takes you through a garden and on to a road at Sycamore Farm **[9]** where you should turn right. Look out for a small stile on the left after a few metres; go over this and a footbridge and keep straight on following the waymarkers over fields then turn right and head towards Knightfields Farm. Go through the gate and head over the field, the tower of Hanbury church should be coming into view. At the next footpath junction, turn left and follow the hedge down to the road and turn right. You come to a road junction where there is a stile off to the left **[10]**. Take this and go down the field and over another stile into the wood. In the wood take the small path which veers to the left and head down the steep hill. Do take care in wet conditions because the path is very slippery. Go over the stile at the bottom of the hill and head left going past Foxholes Cottage **[11]**, over a stile and into a field. Head for the left-hand corner of this field, over another stile and continue to climb up hill with a copse on your left. Go over a third stile, still climbing up the hill and breast the summit. Look behind and admire the views across to Greaves Wood, a mixed deciduous and coniferous woodland. Cross yet another stile and you will see Hanbury church ahead of you. Head towards the trees near the church and admire the views across the Dove valley ahead of you. Cross two more stiles and head to the right, back into Church Lane and to the car park.

Walk 6

Foremark Reservoir and Carver's Rocks

Carboniferous river deltas, Triassic deserts and a Site of Special Scientific Interest

Distance: about 9 km (5.5 miles)
Time: about 3 hours

Carver's Rocks.

This walk starts from the car park **[1]** at Foremark Reservoir, owned by Severn Trent water. From the A514, take the road towards Milton and the reservoir entrance is on the left. There is an automated pay-on-entry system so make sure you have plenty of change. From the car park, walk down to the water's edge and turn left. Here you can see some small outcrops of pebbly Triassic *sandstone* of the Kidderminster Formation **[2]** (p.9). Go back up to the car park and refreshment kiosk. There are a lot of paths to explore in this area and more than one way to reach our next point of call, at Carver's Rocks. Head south from the refreshment kiosk on the path close to the shore. The main route you follow is hilly with quite steep slopes, but there are steps cut into the steepest sections to aid walking. After a little way, you will see a sign on your left-hand side to Carver's Rocks. Take the right-hand of the two paths and continue parallel to the shore. This wooded section of the walk has a wide range of trees and wild flowers **[3]** and you will pass a National Forest interpretation board. Cross a small valley and on the other side, take the right-hand fork in

the path. After entering more woodland you will encounter an interpretation board that provides information concerning the Carver's Rocks Site of Special Scientific Interest (SSSI). Note the outcrops of sandstone along the floor of the path **[4]**. Shortly you will see a cliff of this sandstone and it will be possible to examine it in more detail.

Carver's Rocks has been designated an SSSI due to its ecological importance, with its marshy areas supporting locally important plants. During summer, the marshes are a good place to see reed buntings and the reservoir fringe has breeding great crested grebes. It also contains one of the last areas of heathland in lowland Derbyshire. In open areas, you may hear woodcock on early summer evenings. The reservoir boasts an abundance of butterflies including dingy skipper, brown argus, Essex skipper and purple hairstreak. Carver's Rocks also supports two nationally rare invertebrate species as well as nationally uncommon moths, beetles, hoverflies and sawflies. Some of the flowers you can see include bluebells in the spring and pink foxgloves in the summer.

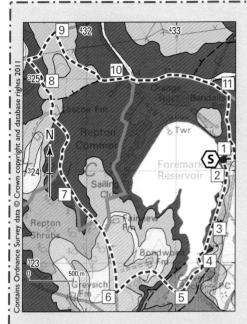

Contains Ordnance Survey data © Crown copyright and database rights 2011

formed an extensive sheet of thick sandstone that spread across the Carboniferous Pennine Basin — today it can also be seen as a prominent feature in the landscape of the Peak District and the Pennines. The crags are covered in lichen, so little is visible of the geological features. However, you will be able to see that the sandstone is generally fine to medium grained and, in places cross-bedding can be observed (pp.8 and 10).

At the end of the crags, continue on down the hill. You will come to a junction in the path and here take the right-hand path. Turn left at a second meeting of paths, proceeding over a bridge and up the hill. About 30 m after the highest point, take a footpath off to your right, going down some steps and across another bridge. You will soon come out of the woodland and into an arable field. Head along the path across this field and then into a pasture field, eventually reaching a gate which you go through. The path runs alongside woodland on your left, crossing more pasture fields. At the end of the woodland, you pass Hartshorn Bog on your left and then you come to a road **[6]**. Turn right here, passing a wood (Repton Shrubs) on your left. Where the road bears off to the right, continue along the track by the wood. Again, note the range of plant life on this section of the walk, with a variety of trees, wild flowers and grasses **[7]**. After about 1 km, the track meets a road and you carry on in the same direction.

The next stage of the walk takes you down a hill with some good exposures of Triassic rocks **[8]**. Near to the top of the hill, patchy exposures of *sandstone* and *mudstone* from the Bromsgrove Sandstone can be observed. Lower

Cross another small valley with a bridge and bear left. After a short distance, take the first path on your right and this will lead you down to the 8–10 m high crags of Carver's Rocks **[5]**. This area is part natural outcrop and part man-made as the rocks were quarried in the 19th century for the construction of local buildings. This outcrop, plus the quarry at Melbourne, apparently provided the best building stone in the area. The name is thought to be associated with Lawrence Carver of Ticknall (born 1701), although in 1836 they were called Repton Rocks and more recently, Dawson's Rocks. The outcrop is composed of crags of Millstone Grit sandstone deposited from a major river delta in Carboniferous times. The rocks are actually made of the youngest (or uppermost) sandstone horizon in the Millstone Grit succession, known as the Rough Rock. This unit

The southern end of Foremark Reservoir near Carver's Rocks.

down the hill, there are some excellent exposures of the Kidderminster Formation where you can see *conglomerates* and *sandstones* (p.9).

Some *cross-bedding* (pp.8 and 10) is visible, showing that the river flowed to the north. Note also the profusion of *quartzite* pebbles in the *conglomerates* and how some of them show graded bedding, that is with large pebbles at the base and progressively smaller pebbles towards the top.

At the bottom of the hill, you come to a road junction. Take the road to the right and climb back up a hill. After about 400 m, you will come to a footpath on your right **[9]**. Follow this, crossing over a track and then stile, to continue along the footpath. As you walk downhill, you pass down from the Bromsgrove Sandstone, on the higher ground, back into the underlying Kidderminster Formation; note that the soil has become very pebbly here **[10]**. The path joins a track; turn left and the track becomes a tarmacked road, then turn right onto another road. Continue along this road for just over 1 km; it is not a busy road but take care to walk on the verges for most of the way. Note the good variety of grasses and wild flowers on the verges and in the neighbouring fields. Just past Bendall's Lodge and Farm, you will come to the right turn into Foremark Reservoir **[11]**. Return to the car park and visitor centre where there are toilets, a refreshment kiosk and plenty of areas for a picnic.

Kidderminster Formation in the road cutting.

Walk 7

The former coal mines of Swannington and Snibston

A legacy of collieries and opencast sites, plus one of England's first railways

Distance: about 8 km (5 miles)
Time: about 2½ hours

The former Snibston Colliery.

This walk commences at the Snibston Discovery Park **[1]**, a major visitor attraction on the site of the former Snibston No.2 Colliery. This mine was opened by George Stephenson in 1832, at the time when he and his son Robert were building the Leicester and Swannington Railway — one of the earliest steam railways in the world, and the first public railway in the Midlands. Snibston produced its last coal in 1983 but the coal mined at the nearby Whitwick Colliery (now the site of Morrison's supermarket) and South Leicester Mine (at Ellistown) continued to be brought to the surface at Snibston until all mining ceased in 1986. This was part of the 'concealed coalfield', where Triassic strata, up to 100 m thick overlie the Coal Measures, so that the coal bearing rocks are not exposed at the surface.

Cars can be parked at the Snibston Discovery centre car park but note that the gates close at 5pm. Walk to the main road and turn left, crossing the road to follow the footpath down the left side of the primary school opposite. Follow through on to the Stephenson's Industrial Estate **[2]** and turn right following the road around in a semi-circle until a footpath is reached leading up and over a timber footbridge crossing the railway. This industrial estate was once the site of a brickworks that utilised the locally mined coal and quarried the red Triassic *mudstones* which crop out here. Once over the bridge, follow the yellow waymarkers leading to the A511, Coalville bypass. Taking care, as this is a busy road, cross to the far side and over the stile to follow the gravel path bearing round to the left. Enter the woodland, and after 20 m turn right at the footpath, up a slope which comprises spoil from the nearby Snibston No.3 Colliery. The path leads to the site of the No.3 mine **[3]** which closed in 1895 following many years of flooding problems. The mounted and preserved colliery winding wheel here

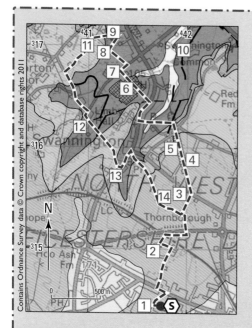

Cross Spring Lane and continue past a length of relaid railway track until you reach the excavated foundations of the Swannington Incline engine house **[4]**. Constructed in 1832, this incline, at 1 in 17 or about 3°, was in use for 115 years. In the early days, coal was transported up the incline to serve the market in Leicester. In the latter days, coal was transported down the incline to the pumping station that was in use to pump water from all the mines that were by now disused. The original Stephenson steam winding engine is now preserved at the National Railway Museum in York. Information boards provide further details on the incline. As you descend the incline, towards Church Lane Bridge, which was renovated in 1994, you will see beds of roughly horizontal brown, Triassic Bromsgrove Sandstone in the sides of the cutting **[5]**.

comes from Ellistown Colliery (closed in 1989), and the smaller wheel was part of the emergency winding gear at Snibston No.2 Colliery. A length of railway track has also been relaid, along the alignment of the old Leicester and Swannington Railway track bed.

Just past the bridge, turn left at the yellow marker post and cross the field towards the junction of Church Lane and Swannington Main Street. You have now reached the outcrop of the Coal

Swannington incline today.

Former railway line on the Swannington incline.

View near Swannington looking across former opencast coal workings. Swannington windmill is in the distance.

Measures strata, although there are no exposures of the typical *mudstones*, *siltstones* and *sandstones* which are the dominant rock types. Turn right and, crossing to the left side of the Main Street, continue for about 200 m until you reach the Village Hall on your left. Immediately past the hall, turn left up a narrow footway until you reach the fields **[6]** where you follow the yellow waymarkers across the fields. The area you are crossing, occupying much of the valley, was the site of the Limby Hall Opencast mine that was worked during the 1940s. The workings were back-filled after the excavation of the coal and the field boundaries have been reinstated so it is difficult to clearly delineate the worked areas. A tell-tale sign is the presence of concrete fence posts used widely to mark the field boundaries following back-filling of the

site. The Five Feet and Minge coal seams were worked here.

On reaching Limby Hall Lane, notice the area of woodland on the north side **[7]**, to your left. This is the site of the Raper and Fenton Mine. Coal was transported along this lane by horse-drawn tramroad to the Charnwood Forest Canal at Thringstone. Turn right down Limby Hall Lane and after 150 m turn left at the footpath sign, head straight up hill following the left side of the hedgerow, do not cross the field diagonally.

When Gorse Field is reached **[8]**, the hummocky scrubland indicates the extensively worked ground, where the Minge Coal seam came to surface. Take time to wander through the site, where information boards have been provided describing the mining methods

Model horse and winding gear for extracting coal from a bellpit. In the background is a former bellpit with winding gear.

used. Numerous shallow pits and bell pits (pp.19 and 20) were sunk to extract the coal. These bell pits would have been served by horse gins to raise the coal to the surface. An example of a reconstructed gin, erected by the Swannington Heritage Trust, is seen in the north-east part of the site. Just beyond the horse gin, 100 m to the east, the site of Califat Colliery **[9]** is marked by a memorial to the miners who died when the workings were flooded in October 1863. Flooding has always been a problem in the Swannington mines, and the Calcutta Colliery **[10]**, 800 m to the east, in the valley at Swannington Common, became the principal pumping station on closure in 1877. It served to drain all the major working mines in the Coalville district, and this continued until the abandonment of Whitwick Colliery in 1986. Looking eastwards across the valley, you may be able to glimpse the Calcutta headstock and pumping house. Together with the Snibston surface buildings and the associated two headstocks, these remain the sole reminders of 20th century mining in the Leicestershire Coalfield.

Follow the main track back through Gorse Field up to the Hough Windmill **[11]** and then turn left along the footpath directly opposite the windmill. Follow the hill crest for about 500 m and turn left down the lane. Before reaching the houses on the east side of the lane, the Five Feet coal seam is inferred as crossing the road. It is not possible to see the coal seam as it is beneath the ground, but geologists have mapped the area and believe that it is present at depth. Ignoring the first turning right, continue for 100 m and then turn right

Headgear of the former Calcutta Pit, Swannington. This pumped all the water out of the Leicestershire coalfield up to 1991.

at the T junction, continuing another 80 m until you see the footpath sign on the left. Walk down the track and cross the small stream to follow the yellow waymarker posts up the hill. The Wilkins Sough, draining water from the nearby Silver Hill Mine emerged in this area [12]. Records of the land hereabouts show coal mining took place as long ago as 1320. As you ascend the hill, you are now rising out of the Coal Measures and walking up the geological timescale into the younger Triassic Mercia Mudstone. You may remember that this was encountered earlier around Coalville and at the top of the Swannington Incline. Crossing over the hill crest, follow the footpath sign to the right of the field and descend onto an old bridleway where Triassic sandstones can be seen in the cutting [13]. Farther down, the path cuts into the older Coal Measures rocks, but these are so weathered they are not readily recognisable.

On reaching the Swannington Main Street, turn left and then right at the Robin Hood Inn. Passing the right hand side of the pub, follow the left public byway. After 100 m, we have again passed upwards in time from the Coal Measures into the Triassic strata. About 500 m along this track, the steep rising ground on your left is all that remains of the spoil tip from the Snibston No.3 Colliery [14]. You have now completed the circular route and can therefore retrace your steps across the A511, through the industrial estate and back to the Snibston Discovery Park. If time is available, the Discovery Park is well worth a visit, with much information on the mining and geology of the district on display. There are also tours of the surface buildings of the old colliery, which give an excellent insight into what was once the most important industry of north-west Leicestershire.

Walk 8

A walk to examine the building stones of Burton upon Trent

Parking: There are a number of car parks in the town centre; the Meadowside Centre car park off the High Street is most convenient

Distance: about 6.6 km (about 4 miles). You can shorten the walk by missing out St Chad's Church [19]. It is possible to drive here and park in the surrounding streets for free
Time: about 2 hours
This walk is suitable for the disabled.

The town of Burton upon Trent is most famous for its long history as a centre of the brewing industry. Although Burton was settled by monks as far back as the 11th century, it was the later growth of the brewing industry which really created much of the town we see today. Its location at a strategic crossing point of the River Trent, a major commercial 'highway' since medieval times, was clearly an attraction prior to the arrival of the canal and railway networks in 1839.

Burton is dominated by largely 18th and 19th century red-brick developments, but dig deeper and it is possible to find a small but interesting range of buildings constructed of stones of varying types. These building stones span much of the geological column, ranging from Precambrian to the Middle Jurassic in age. Sadly little remains today of the original abbey and its massive cathedral-like stone church.

Burton upon Trent from Tower Woods.

Photograph © Christopher Beech, courtesy of NFC

The trail begins at the site of the 19th century bridge spanning the River Trent [1]. Walking here from the Meadowside car park, you can see some fine Georgian architecture at the junction of the High Street and Horninglow Street.

BRIDGE STREET

1 Trent bridge

The present bridge which is 140 m (460 yards) in length was completed in 1864. It replaced an even more impressive medieval structure of 36 arches that was apparently constructed of local *sandstones* quarried nearby from the Triassic Bromsgrove Sandstone Formation, 'a mile downstream on the Derbyshire side of the Trent'. The present bridge is constructed of a different material, very large sandstone blocks from the Millstone Grit Group. These blocks are typically very coarse grained, *cross-bedded* (pp.8 and 10), quartz-rich sandstones and show a range of colours from greenish grey to buff and orange-brown. You can see small pebbles in some of the sandstone

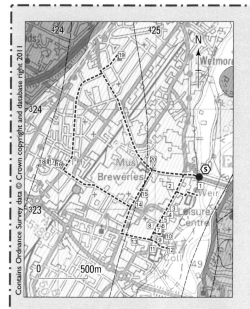

number of different *igneous intrusions* that were emplaced into the Earth's crust in the Carboniferous Period.

HIGH STREET

2 Congregational chapel (now the Riverside church).

This chapel was constructed in 1842 of local red bricks and buff-coloured Bromsgrove Sandstone. This sandstone is used only for the main building facade and shows a fine range of distinctive sedimentary structures. These include *cross-bedding* (pp.8 and 10) and areas where the bedding was deformed when it was a wet sediment. Compare and contrast this sandstone with that seen in the bridge.

3 Worthington brewery office

This predominantly red brick building has, like many similar 19th century buildings along the High Street, stone dressings of pale buff-coloured Carboniferous sandstone. The prominent sandstone porch shows a shield and dagger carved above the entrance — still the trade mark of Worthington Beer.

4 Constitutional Club

The red brick and decoratively carved buff sandstone facade was clearly designed to impress potential members. The hard, fine-to medium-grained, quartz-rich sandstone is probably from the Millstone Grit.

5 NatWest Bank

The construction of a classically designed lower facade to this building at street level was built in the 19th century and intentionally designed to emphasise the solidity and stability

blocks. Despite the fact that a significant supply of the sandstone was required, the precise quarry source in Derbyshire has not been identified.

Kerbstones. Throughout the trail look carefully at the kerbing stones used on the bridge and indeed elsewhere along the High Street and on many of the surviving older thoroughfares. On the bridge and elsewhere, they consist of a distinctive dark red, coarse-grained, *igneous rock* known as a *granodiorite*, quarried at Mountsorrel on the eastern side of Charnwood Forest. This quarry is still active for crushed aggregate but in the 19th century, it was a major supplier of kerbing and stone setts across the Midlands and even as far afield as London. As you move along the High Street several other igneous rocks can be seen as kerbing stones, including dark green, pale grey and greenish grey varieties. All were sourced from a

 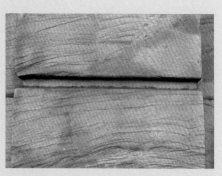

Contrasting sandstone building blocks: on the left, Millstone Grit in the wall of Trent Bridge, Burton. Note the clear parallel lamination and cross-bedding (pp.8 and 10) in the blocks. On the right, finer-grained Bromsgrove Sandstone, seen in several buildings.

of the bank. Constructed of pale buff-coloured Triassic Bromsgrove Sandstone it is now showing some areas of decay. A range of features can be seen within the sandstone blocks.

6 Old cinema

By the end of the 19th Century, problems arising from industrial pollution affected Burton and many other urban centres. The soot-blackened facades of some buildings prompted substitution of the stone with glazed terracotta tiles. The remaining portion of the upper facade of this building shows why these pollution resistant 'tiles' were used.

7 Barclays Bank

The modern lower facade of this bank is decorated at pavement level with polished slabs of a very distinctive coarsely crystalline igneous rock. It is called *Larvikite*, and is only available from a single quarry in Norway. The upper facade of white Portland Stone was quarried from the Jurassic *limestones* of Portland Bill in Dorset.

8 HSBC and Lloyds banks

Again the facade of these banks is designed to demonstrate solidity and stability. They are constructed of pinkish buff, coarse grained, Millstone Grit sandstone. Lloyds Bank additionally has columns of distinctive red coarse-grained Scottish granite at both entrances.

Lloyds Bank building in Burton High Street. This is constructed using Millstone Grit sandstione but note the distinctive columns made of Scottish granite.

9 Market Hall (1883)

Opened on the 24 October 1883, the Market Hall was designed and constructed by the Barnsley architects Dixon and Moxon for the princely sum of £12 000. Roddis of Birmingham used a buff-coloured Carboniferous Millstone Grit to carve the striking decorated mouldings, one with a large bull's head. The source of the sandstone has yet to be established but in view of the Barnsley base of the architects, a South Yorkshire rather than Derbyshire origin seems likely.

10 Church of St Modwen (1719)

This massive early 18th Century church was designed and built by the Smith family from Warwickshire. It is constructed of red and 'white' (p.29) Triassic *sandstones*, similar in character to those still quarried at Hollington in north Staffordshire. On these blocks there are a variety of sedimentary features including *cross-bedding* (pp.8 and 10) and *mudstone* fragments (clasts), some of which have occasionally weathered out leaving a pock-marked surface. The sandstone paving stones on the north side of the church are of Yorkshire stone, probably from the famous Elland Flags Formation near Halifax. The graveyard at the back of the church includes several headstones of purple Welsh slate from the Penrhyn Quarries in north Wales.

11 War memorial

This elaborate memorial to victims of the Great War is built using Portland Stone, and the bronze was cast and carved by Henry Fehr. The white Portland Stone used, is one of England's most distinctive building stones and was quarried from the Jurassic limestones of Portland Bill. This is an *ooidal* limestone, a rock made from small spheres of carbonate, called ooids.

12 The Winery or 'Abbey' Inn

Tucked away along the riverside behind the Market Hall is one of Burton upon Trent's surviving architectural gems. Standing on part of the site of the former Benedictine Burton Abbey and possibly part of the original infirmary, this picturesque timber-framed house was greatly altered in the Victorian period, but also contains older stone remnants believed to be part of the original abbey. The building

Market Hall in Burton with the distinctive carved bull's head. The stone frontage is built of Millstone Grit sandstone.

The war memorial in Burton upon Trent, built of Portland Stone.

is constructed from pale red to buff and greenish grey Triassic sandstone of probable local origin. Whether these stones were perhaps recycled from the original abbey fabric is open to debate. However, significant volumes of stone would have been available after the dissolution of the abbey, so it is possible that they were reused here. The best views of this building are achieved from the back, by the riverside.

NEW STREET

13 Corporation fire station

Built in 1905 from Triassic sandstones. Take the next right (*Union Street*); at the second left turning (*Station Street*), immediately on your right is:

14 County Court

This solid-looking stone building is constructed of large blocks of coarse Carboniferous sandstone. Back at the crossroads, just along to your right is:

15 Trinity Methodist church

This impressive classically fronted Methodist church is constructed principally of red brick with elaborate sandstone dressings. The buff coloured stonework is composed of Carboniferous sandstone. This building was constructed on a very large scale and the sedimentary structures, such as the *cross-bedding* (pp.8 and 10), appear to have been arranged in decorative patterns.

Go back to the crossroads and turn right into Station Street, continuing past the station along Borough Road to the next locality in *King Edward's Square*.

The newer, yellowed Portland Stone facade of the 1938–39 municipal offices with the older Victorian (1878) Town Hall clock tower facade of pale Lincolnshire Limestone (Ancaster Stone) and red brick.

The 'Abbey Inn' with its Triassic dressed sandstone stone blockwork. It contains part of the original Benedictine Burton Abbey Infirmary. It is on the river just south of the Market Hall.

16 Town Hall

This is a fine example of decorative Victorian architecture funded by the Bass brewing family. It was originally the St Paul's church institute, before becoming the Town Hall in 1894. The fabric is a combination of red brick with contrasting, elaborate pale-coloured limestone dressings. The very distinctive nature of this shelly ooidal limestone with its 'stripy' texture (sometimes termed streaky bacon) suggests it is from the Ancaster quarries (Jurassic Lincolnshire Limestone Formation), near Grantham in Lincolnshire.

17 Municipal buildings

Designed by George Moncur and completed by 1939, this later addition shows a complete change of architectural style and materials. Brown brick dominates the main fabric but dressings of white and yellowed Portland Stone replace the Lincolnshire Limestone of the earlier buildings. In the same square, you can see:

18 St Paul's parish church

Designed and constructed in 1874 by the architects J M Teale and E B Denison (Lord Grimethorpe), this very large church complements the architecture of the 'old' Town Hall but uses different building materials. The main wall stones in the church are brown medium- to coarse-grained, quartz-rich sandstones of Millstone Grit from Coxbench Quarry in Derbyshire. In contrast the elaborate decorative dressings are the same pale yellow Lincolnshire Limestone (Ancaster Stone) that was also used in the Town Hall.

An interesting point of note in this church is the juxtaposition of limestone with sandstone. It is common wisdom among many architects, and some building stone specialists that it is a mistake to place two mineralogically different stones together in a building, as it could potentially accelerate stone decay. In this 136-year-old building, however, there appears to have been no deleterious effect, most of the stonework looking as new.

For the shorter walk, head back past the station to the crossroads by the County Court. Turn left into Guild Street and at the junction with Horninglow Street, on the opposite side of the road are:

19 Magistrates Court

Designed and constructed by the Burton architect Henry Beck, this striking, classically styled building with its leaded dome is constructed wholly of white Portland Stone. The stonework is of a high quality and shows well the ooidal fabric of the limestone, with concentrations of mollusc shells. The Portland Stone used here has probably been extensively cleaned up in recent decades, but it does emphasise the resistance of this stone to urban pollution and degradation. Turn left down Horninglow Road and you will return back to the High Street.

For the longer walk, return past the Town Hall and turn left into Wellington Street and continue into Waterloo Street and Victoria Crescent. At the junction with Horninglow Road, cross over into Hunter Street and just to the left you will come to:

20 St Chad's church

Set amongst rows of red brick terraces, this striking red sandstone church, built of Bromsgrove Sandstone, was designed by the famous Victorian church architect George Fredrick Bodley. It was built between 1903 and 1910 for the Bass Brewing family. At first glance the strong red colour of the sandstone dominates, but higher in the structure a far more decorative element is evident around its elaborately carved windows and belfry openings. The almost detached bell tower is a unique feature. The dramatic red colouration of the stone used may not be typical Staffordshire Hollington Stone, which generally has a paler mottled coloration. Possibly, the sandstone used is the Triassic Runcorn Stone from Cheshire. This was a building stone that Bodley had used earlier in his design for a church at Clumber Park in Nottinghamshire, constructed for the Duke of Newcastle between 1886 and 1889.

St Chad's church.

Walk 9

Thornton to Bagworth circular walk

Distance: about 8 km (5 miles)
Time: about 2½ hours

View over Thornton reservoir.

The walk starts from the car park at Thornton Reservoir [1], but being a circular walk could also commence from Bagworth Heath Woods car park, where free parking is also provided. Thornton Reservoir was constructed by the Leicester Water Board in 1854 as the first reservoir in the county to supply water to the city. The water is now piped to Cropston Reservoir, 10 km to the east.

The reservoir is underlain by the Mercia Mudstone Group, mainly consisting of impervious red Triassic *mudstones*

Desford brick clay pit in the Mercia Mudstone Group.

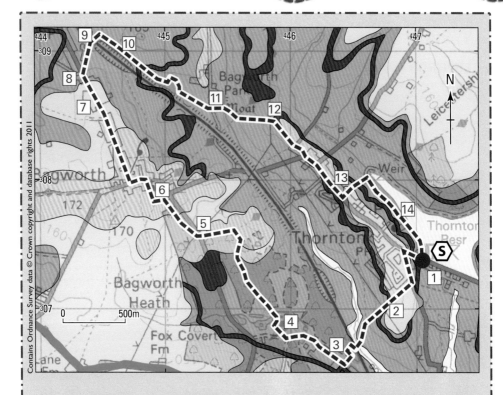

but with harder *beds* of *sandstone* and *siltstone* that form features on the landscape. One such prominent bed is the Cotgrave Sandstone (formerly known as the 'Thornton Skerry') and it forms the hill on which the village of Thornton is situated. On leaving the car park, turn right into Reservoir Road and as you approach the T junction you are walking over the landform created by the Cotgrave Sandstone. Turn left at the T junction into Merrylees Road and continue to the end of the built up zone where you turn right along the signed footpath. When you start to descend the hill **[2]** keep on the left side of the hedgerow and go straight down the hill, heading towards the brickworks across the valley. Looking

back, and to your left, you can see how the harder sandstone layer has created a marked escarpment on the hillside.

Follow the yellow waymarker posts and cross the small footbridge over a stream, then immediately cross the railway, taking great care to observe the 'stop, look and listen' instructions. This is the route of the Leicester and Swannington Railway, the first major standard gauge steam railway in the Midlands, completed between Leicester and Bagworth in July 1832. Note the sandstone steps either side of the railway track that consist of the original stone railway sleeper blocks.

Pass round to the right of the balancing pond and head directly towards the

Desford brickworks fence boundary **[3]** where you turn right along the track. Balancing ponds were constructed to control flood waters in river valleys. The Thringstone Fault lies beneath you at this point, and runs in a north westerly direction roughly paralleling to the railway line. This *fault* is a major fracture in the Earth's crust, separating the much older Charnian rocks to the east from the Carboniferous Coal Measures to the west. At this point, the hill rising to your right consists of colliery spoil from the nearby former Desford Colliery. Walk up this slope to gain a view across the brickworks and the associated clay pit, cut deep into the hillside. The red Triassic mudstone brick clay (p.25) visible in the quarry face is about 100 m in thickness and sits on top of the Coal Measures to the west of the Thringstone Fault. Today, the only way to see the coal-bearing strata is in the spoil material from the old colliery. This reveals a variety of rocks, including grey shaly mudstones, siltstones and sandstones together with sporadic coal fragments. On some of the mudstone surfaces, fossilised plant fragments may be found.

Follow the path between the brickworks boundary and the spoil tip and you soon emerge into the area now landscaped as Bagworth Heath Woods. This 75 hectare woodland (185 acres) was once the site of the large Desford Colliery, which closed in 1984. About 200 m after passing the line of tall conifers, and just before the path opens into grassland, the former sites of the two Desford Colliery shafts are indicated by large concrete marker

Concrete block marking the site of the Desford Colliery mine shaft. The manhole in the foreground covers the shaft.

blocks **[4]** amongst the bushes a few metres to your right. These shafts, sunk in 1900, were both 4.25 m in diameter and reached a depth of 199 m, from where the Lower Main Seam was worked.

As you walk across the grassed area, you will encounter the metalled path which leads to the right and up the hill to the north. Before following this path, you may wish to walk farther across the grass to the small lakes, where an information board provides some details of the former colliery. The lakes and the area to the west

Bagworth church. The old Norman church here collapsed due to mining subsidence. It was rebuilt in 1968.

resulted from mining subsidence, known as 'subsidence flashes', and they provide wetland habitats for wildfowl and aquatic plants. A row of houses along the nearby Heath Road were also badly damaged by the subsidence and had to be demolished. After closure of Desford Colliery, the whole area was landscaped and became the Bagworth Heath Woods. Up the hill (landscaped colliery waste) to the north of the valley, the path goes through trial planting areas of native species woodland. This demonstration woodland shows different techniques for woodland establishment and maintenance on reclaimed colliery spoil. As you continue along this track you emerge from Bagworth Heath Woods into a new woodland area, Manor Wood, where an information board describes the planting. After 200 m, the path meets the long-distance footpath, the 'Leicestershire Round'. Turn left and follow the Leicestershire Round for about 250 m until you meet Heath Road [5]. At this location, a number of houses and terraced miner's cottages once existed, known as Little Bagworth. No trace of this settlement remains, again following extensive mining subsidence damage, all were demolished.

Cross the road and immediately follow the signposted arrow to the right,

Subsidence flash at Bagworth Heath with the old Desford Colliery headstock wheel on the island.

towards Bagworth. Follow the yellow waymarkers through the gate and into the church graveyard, then across to the next waymarker and turn right following the outer boundary of the church land. Bagworth church **[6]** is modern, replacing the old Norman church that was severely damaged by mining subsidence in 1968. Cross the road, turning left and continue up the hill to the junction with Station Road, where you turn right, following the long straight road through Bagworth. About 600 m along this road, you will notice the extensive area of newish housing on the left hand side, all built on the former site of Bagworth Colliery **[7]**. There is also a miner's memorial alongside the road and behind, the main shafts to the colliery were located. They are now the site of the children's play area.

Bagworth Colliery (p.19) had a long history; the first shafts were sunk in 1825, and the colliery was the last

north-west Leicestershire mine to close in February 1991. The presence of many thick coal seams, and the adoption of modern mining methods following nationalisation, resulted in high efficiency. However, extensive coal removal also created the wide-spread problem of mining subsidence, and many buildings were damaged beyond repair and unusual features were created on the landscape. One such feature is the marked slope change in Station Road, close to its junction with Park Lane **[8]**. Turn right here, and follow Park Lane until you reach the footbridge over the railway. Looking north from this bridge **[9]**, the scenery in days past would have been very different. The whole area to the left of the present line was an extensive array of railway sidings serving Bagworth Colliery, with Bagworth and Ellistown Railway Station (closed in 1964) near to the footbridge seen in the distance. The view ahead would have included the prominent buildings, chimneys and headgears of Ellistown Colliery, which closed in 1989. Here can be seen the Ellistown brick and tile works, part of the Ibstock Brick Company (p.27). Bardon Hill forms the skyline with a telecommunications relay station on its summit. It is the highest point in Leicestershire at 278 m above sea level, comprising hard Precambrian rocks which continue to be extensively quarried,

Turn right after crossing the footbridge and you come to the top of the Bagworth Incline. When the original Leicester and Swannington Railway was constructed in 1832, the track alignment included a 1 km-long incline

[10] at a gradient of 2°, which had an Incline Keeper's House at the top. Although a Grade 2 listed building, this was allowed to fall into disrepair and collapsed in recent years. The incline worked on the principle of gravity — the weight of full wagons (loaded with coal or rock) descending the incline pulled the empty ones back up to be refilled. In 1848, the railway was realigned and a more sensible gentle rise to Bagworth was achieved by the construction of embankments, viaducts, bridges and excavations of cuttings between Thornton Mill and Bagworth Station. Descend the incline, now a pleasant wide 'green lane', and on reaching the bottom, follow the yellow arrows across the road leading to Bagworth Park Estate [11] (the former home of Lord Maynard, original developer of the Bagworth Colliery). You have now crossed over to the east side of the pre-Triassic Thringstone Fault and because the Coal Measures strata are no longer present at depth, there is no evidence of any mining or related subsidence. Cross the field, over the small stream and skirt the left side of the field until you reach a stile. Step over and immediately bear right, heading up the hill towards the electricity pylon where you can enter Thornton Plantation [12], part of The National Forest's broadleaved native planting scheme. Started in 1998, the trees are already becoming well established. You are now back on the hill top underlain by the relatively hard Cotgrave Sandstone.

As you approach Thornton Main Street, notice the stone walls contain large blocks of *diorite* and Charnian

Miners' memorial at Bagworth Colliery.

rocks, which were most likely quarried from the outcrops near to Markfield and Stanton under Bardon. Proceed straight along the Main Street until you reach the primary school on your left. Immediately past the this school, turn left [13] back on to the Leicestershire Round. Away from the Main Street, the hill slopes down towards the reservoir, which can be reached by passing through the hedge beyond the playing fields and then on to the main reservoir path round to the right. Refreshments and toilets can be found at the visitor centre [14] 300 m farther along this path. Beyond this, a tarmacked road leads you back to your starting point, the reservoir car park [15].

Walk 10

Ticknall to Staunton Harold Hall and back

Distance: about 12 km (7.75 miles)
Time: half a day but you may want to make a full day and visit Calke Abbey. There is also a garden centre at Staunton Harold Hall

Equipment: bring a torch if you intend to walk through the Ticknall Tramway tunnel

Gigantoproductus. *One of the fossils that may be found in the Ticknall limeyards.*

Not suitable for people with walking difficulties as there are steps on some sections of the walk.

The walk can easily be split into two shorter circuits; by parking at Staunton Harold or one of the car parks by Staunton Harold Reservoir (locations 12 and 13 on the map) you can cut out over a mile of walking through the village of Ticknall.

This walk can easily be started at either Ticknall or Staunton Harold Hall as there is good parking at both places. For Ticknall, drive through the village and look for the car park at the village hall [1] on the north side of the village, clearly signposted from the main road. It is also possible to park at other car parks along the route [12, 13] (see map) and all are currently free.

From the car park in Ticknall, head back to the main road and turn left. Go through the village and when you are almost at the end, opposite the last house on the left-hand side, turn right onto a tarmacked track into the former Ticknall limeyards. These lime quarries exisited on both sides of the main road through the village and worked *limestones* and *mudstones* of Carboniferous age. Ticknall was also once home to a flourishing pottery industry in the 16th to the 19th centuries (p.25). You can still find old pottery debris in the fields around the village.

Continue along the track for a short distance until you reach a field on your right then take a path off to your left. After a short walk down you will see a major arch of rock below which there is a cave [2]. This is man-made and the limestone was mined here and in other parts of the limeworks (p.27). The more intrepid walkers can scramble down the bank and take a closer look at the cave. Return to the track and head back the way you came. After a short distance, take a path off to your left and head into the Ticknall Lime Yards SSSI and through the main quarries. Please note the sign warning about the potential hazards and also that hammering of the rock faces is not allowed. To your left

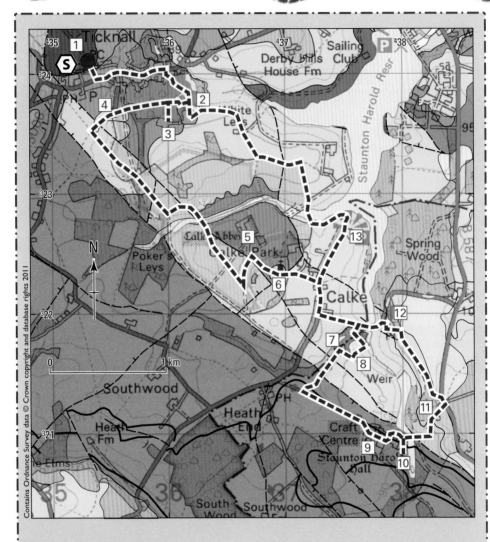

you can see a quarry face composed of a well-bedded yellowish rock called dolostone (p.6). Just ahead you come to a buttress of this rock. It is not a particularly fossiliferous rock as many of the fossils were destroyed in the alteration process to dolomite. This is the main mineral that makes up the dolostone rock. Immediately past the

buttress, turn left and head down the path for a short distance. You will come to another rock face **[3]** that again shows good, near-horizontal bedding, it also contains some *beds* of *mudstone* and pure white *limestone* at the bottom. Look to your right and you will see a large block of rock that is dipping quite steeply towards the face. This is

Well-bedded limestones and mudstones of the Ticknall Limestone Formation exposed in the former limeworks at Ticknall.

Collapsed block of limestone in the Ticknall limeyards.

actually a block from the collapse of a former mine here.

Return to the main path and turn left, continuing through the old quarries and note the large piles of quarry spoil here. You will pass rock pillars and go under a bridge — tall people beware, but there is an avoiding path. Soon you will come to a tunnel **[4]**. This was where the Ticknall Tramway (p.28) entered the quarries. It was built so the tramway avoided crossing the road to Calke Abbey and is considered to be one of the oldest railway arches in the world. To avoid walking through the tunnel, take a path off to the left just before the entrance, cross over the road to Calke Abbey and continue

Calke Abbey church.

on to a gate. Go through the gate and after about 30 m take a path on your left, joining up with the tunnel route. If you go through the tunnel take care as the floor is uneven and slippery and the roof height is very variable. At the end of the tunnel, ascend the steps on your left, cross over two stiles and take the right-hand of the two paths.

The next section of the walk passes through pasture fields that may contain sheep. You will come to a wall which you cross using a stile, climb over a second stile and across a field to turn right on the road to Calke Abbey. Continue along the road, go over a cattle grid and climb up the hill ahead. You are climbing up a slope formed by a bed of resistant *sandstone* in the Millstone Grit. At the crest of the hill, continue down the other side — the gentler gradient shows that you are descending what is called a dip slope, caused by tilting of this bed of sandstone. Where the road bends to the left, you will need to continue straight ahead along a path. At the bottom of the slope, turn left along a grass track. Soon, Calke Abbey [5] will come into view (p.35) and you will join the tarmacked road leading away from the Abbey. If you would like to visit the abbey, turn left.

If you are not visiting the abbey, turn right along this road. You will pass the church on your left [6] but access is only possible from the abbey and gardens. Continue along the exit road from the abbey until you reach a normal road and then turn right. This road is quiet as it mainly serves visitor traffic leaving the abbey. At the next junction, turn left and after about 300 m, you will come to a bend with a signpost and turn off to the right here into Dimminsdale **[7]**. Dimminsdale is a 6.5 hectare nature reserve owned by Severn Trent Water and managed by the Leicestershire and Rutland Wildlife Trust. The varied geology has resulted in a good mix of habitats — scrub, damp woodland, open water and glades. Interpretation boards provide information on the flora and birdlife of

the reserve — you may be lucky and spot a kingfisher here. In early spring, the nature reserve is also noted for its fabulous display of snowdrops. However, please note that the paths may be muddy.

Dimminsdale was formerly another area of limeyards (p.29) that was also connected to the Ticknall Tramway, but opening later in 1830. Coal was also brought here by the tramway to fire the lime kilns, from the nearby, now-disused, colliery in Rough Heath Wood. Sadly, none of the former lime quarries are now visible as they are all submerged under water. On p.28 is an artist's representation of what they looked like

Photograph © Christopher Beech, courtesy of NFC

Snowdrops at Dimminsdale, a nature reserve near Calke. The reserve is owned by Severn Trent Water and managed by the Leicestershire and Rutland Wildlife Trust.

Staunton Harold Hall.

in their heyday. The remains of some of the lime kilns are still visible.

After a short distance descend a series of steps to a junction in the path. Take the left-hand path and after a while you will come to a post with the number 6 on it. Just off to the right here and ahead, you will see a rock face **[8]**. This is a bed of pebbly sandstone in the Millstone Grit. These strata overlie and are therefore younger than the limestones worked in the quarries. They form what is known as the quarry 'overburden', or waste material that had to be removed prior to quarrying

the limestone. It is not known whether this sandstone was worked at all but it may have been used for dry stone walls, as was sandstone quarried from near Calke Abbey.

At the far side of the nature reserve, take the footpath off to the left and continue along a grass path until you reach a road. Turn left here towards Staunton Harold Hall **[9]** (p.34). Just before you reach this road, you will cross over the Thringstone Fault, the major structure that marks the northern boundary of the Leicestershire Coalfield; so you are now walking on rocks of the Carboniferous Coal Measures. In the past, coal was mined from the nearby village of Heath End for use on the Staunton Harold Estate.

At Staunton Harold, you may like to look around and visit the garden centre. The hall, built between 1760 and 1778, is not open to the public but there is an attractive church [10]. This church, managed by the National Trust, is only open on specific days, so it is best to check on the National Trust website when planning your visit.

Exit via the road crossing the lake in front of the hall, where there is often a good variety of bird life. Take a footpath immediately on your left, continuing up the hill and entering the wood on your left, known as Keith's Clump [11]. This is a permissive path, so please read the notice and follow all instructions given. Follow the path through the wood, continuing beyond along a lengthy stretch with a wall to your left. Here, we have crossed over an *unconformity* representing a time gap of about 70 million years, and are now on the Triassic Bromsgrove Sandstone Formation. In the field to your right, you may be able to see blocks of this sandstone. Soon you will come to a stile

on your left and after crossing it, take the path going downhill through more woodland. There are good views to your left looking back towards Staunton Harold Hall.

At the bottom, you will come to a car park [12]; turn left and exit in the left corner onto a road, turning left and crossing the southern tip of Staunton Harold Reservoir. You have now returned to Dimminsdale; retrace your steps up the hill, turning right and past the exit road from Calke Abbey. Continue down to another car park [13], which has excellent views over the reservoir and an interpretation board giving details of the wildlife. Exit the car park and continue along the path from the end of the road, down to the reservoir shore and turn left along the shore. Cross over the shallow water and the path runs parallel to a wire fence on your left marking the boundary of the Calke Estate. Cross a stile at the end of the fence and continue on for about 40 m, then take a path off to your right. The path now crosses a number of fields and you may see blocks of sandstone in these fields, derived from the Millstone Grit. You will eventually come back to the track through the Ticknall limeyards. Follow this back to the main road, turn left and head back to the car park.

The National Forest

A forest in the making

Embracing 200 square miles at the heart of England, The National Forest is taking root across parts of Derbyshire, Leicestershire and Staffordshire. It is one of the biggest and boldest initiatives in the UK; transforming the landscape with the aim of linking the ancient Forest of Charnwood on its eastern fringe with Needwood Forest to its west. Within its boundary lie miles of rolling farmland and the former Leicestershire and South Derbyshire Coalfield, which was in desperate need of both environmental and economic regeneration. Forest towns include Burton upon Trent (famous for its brewing industry), Coalville and Swadlincote (formerly associated with mining and pottery) and the historic market town of Ashby-de-la-Zouch.

The idea, first conceived in the late 1980s, was to transform one of the country's least wooded regions into an area with a rich mosaic of land uses, framed by woodland, for the pleasure and benefit of the community, landscape and environment. The ambitious goal for The National Forest is to increase woodland cover to about a third of all the land within its boundary. This is now well under way, with woodland cover having increased from around 6 per cent in 1991 to more than 18 per cent in 2010. As a result, large swathes of countryside are now more accessible to local people and visitors with over 80 per cent of woodland sites open to all, to be explored and enjoyed. In order to create a diverse forest of predominantly broadleaved character, approximately 87 per cent of the trees planted to date are broadleaf species.

Photograph © Christopher Beech, courtesy of NFC

Many individuals and organisations are involved in the creation of the Forest — local people, private landowners, public and voluntary sector bodies, private businesses and people from all over the country. Spearheading the initiative is The National Forest Company, established by Government in 1995 and sponsored by the Department for Environment, Food and Rural Affairs (Defra). The Company is responsible, through working with partners, for the delivery of the Government-approved National Forest Strategy — the vision for the Forest.

Creating a new landscape takes ambition, time and sensitivity. Over 7.8 million trees have already been planted, 'greening' more than 6200 hectares (15 300 acres) of derelict coalfield land and mineral workings and converting farmland to woodland. Other wildlife habitats are also being created or brought back into proper management (more than 1700 ha by 2010). The rural economy is stimulated through diversification into a wide range of new enterprises and new jobs are being created, especially at visitor attractions that are part of a rapidly growing tourism sector. Uses for the timber itself are being explored to ensure the woodland economy is viable and therefore sustainable.

Given all of this, The National Forest is a vast working example of sustainable development, fulfilling environmental, social and economic objectives for present and future generations. The National Forest is:

- blending new and maturing woodland within a wide variety of landscapes, presenting opportunities for many to take part in its development

- an inspiring example for the country, in the face of climate change and other environmental pressures

- a place of enjoyment and learning for its residents and visitors

- a place of contrasts, where people find quiet relaxation and active leisure

- a working forest providing new and sustainable livelihoods

- enriching the lives of people, the landscape and wildlife.

Photograph © The National Forest Company

Get involved

There are many ways that you can take part in the creation of The National Forest.

Individuals can contribute in many ways: by planting a tree or leaving a legacy or by making a major gift in memory of someone you love or to mark one of life's special occasions.

Community and environmental groups have many opportunities to take an active role in the Forest's creation. These range from volunteering for practical conservation work, community tree planting projects and maintenance of local woods to marking your place in the Forest with a distinctive arts or heritage feature. Whatever your interest, you can contribute your expertise and energy. Grants are available to support many community activities.

Schools within and around the Forest can use a range of excellent education centres and all-weather facilities, which cater for all ages and key stages throughout this huge outdoor classroom.

Landowners (existing and aspiring) can gain funding via one of our grant schemes, such as the unique Changing Landscapes Scheme (CLS), to create their own woodland in the Forest.

Although The National Forest Company has Government backing, we are particularly keen to work with the **private sector** and have a variety of ways that you can help through partnership working, sponsorship (financial and in-kind) and staff engagement.

Voluntary bodies and charities work with us on joint projects to realise the Forest's ambitious aims and make this 'a Forest for the nation'.

Whether with your family, in a group of friends or as a lone explorer, there's a wealth of walks, attractions and delights **for visitors** to discover and enjoy in The National Forest.

National Forest walks

Whether you are looking for an afternoon stroll through the trees or a challenging 15 mile walk across changing landscapes, The National Forest is the place for you. Whatever your ability, there is something for everyone. There are over 200 woodlands with public access, mile after mile of footpaths to navigate or, if you don't want to work out your own route, there are dozens of walks available via The National Forest website (www.nationalforest.org).

The National Forest Company has also produced a series of guides giving information on walks and accessible sites within the Forest. The guides are split into four categories: *Short Walks* (less than 5 miles), *Medium Walks* (5 to 10 miles), *Long Walks* (more than 10 miles) and *Access for All* (specifically designed to provide information on sites and attractions that are suitable for all abilities).

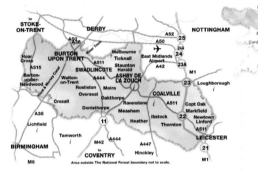

Location map of The National Forest.

© The National Forest Company

Photograph © Christopher Beech, courtesy of NFC

Each leaflet gives clear, concise directions together with an Ordnance Survey map showing the route. They also provide information about some of the sights along the way and some historical background to the area. All of the walking guides are available from main tourist information centres in the Forest or to download from The National Forest website. We are constantly adding or updating walks so keep checking back for the latest information.

National Forest and beyond

The visitor and attractions guides are updated annually and provide further information on woodland sites, visitor attractions, activities and accommodation in and around The National Forest area.

Find out more

For more information on The National Forest, places to visit, walking, cycling, horse-riding, wildlife, events, grants available, planting a tree and how to get involved visit: www.nationalforest.org

For further information on The National Forest or for details of all National Forest leaflets and guides contact:

The National Forest Company, Enterprise Glade, Bath Lane, Moira, Swadlincote, Derbyshire DE12 6BA.
Tel: 01283 551211
Fax: 01283 552844

Website: www.nationalforest.org
Email: enquiries@nationalforest.org

GEOLOGICAL GLOSSARY

Alluvium Loose deposits of clay, silt, sand and gravel laid down on *floodplains* by the action of rivers in the recent past.

Aquifer Layers or lenses of permeable rock or unconsolidated sediments below or on the Earth's surface capable of storing and yielding water.

Bed An individual layer of sediment or a stratum of *sedimentary rock*.

Conglomerate Dominantly a rock comprised of well-rounded pebbles and sand grains.

Crinoid Fossilised remains of shelly marine creatures, related to sea urchins, usually attached by a stem composed of discs (ossicles).

Cross-bedding *also known* **as current-bedding** A feature of *sedimentary rocks* formed by the movement of sand grains in currents to produce layering oblique to the margins of the *beds*.

Deformation Any natural process that bends, twists or fractures rocks.

Diorite A medium- to coarse-grained intrusive *igneous rock* composed principally of the minerals *plagioclase feldspar*, hornblende, and/or pyroxene.

Dolomitic, dolomitised Descriptive terms for a limestone that has had some of its calcium carbonate replaced by magnesium carbonate.

Erosional unconformity (see *'unconformity'*)

Fault, faulting Fractures in the rocks that formed as a result of movements triggered by earthquakes.

Feldspar A commonly occurring aluminium silicate mineral of potassium, sodium and calcium.

Floodplain The flattish floor of a valley composed of *alluvium* and prone to flooding.

Granodiorite A coarse-grained intrusive *igneous rock* similar to granite, but with more *plagioclase feldspar* than potassium *feldspar*.

Igneous rock Rock formed when molten *magma* cools and solidifies. It includes extrusive rocks erupted from volcanoes (e.g. andesite) and intrusive rocks that cool beneath the Earth's surface (e.g. *diorite*).

Intrusion A body of *igneous rock* formed from molten *magma* that has been introduced into pre-existing rock.

Laminae, lamination, laminated The narrowest type of layering in *sedimentary rocks*, less than 1 cm in thickness.

Larvikite A coarse grained, intrusive igneous rock named after the town of Larvik in Norway where it is found. Alternations of different *feldspar* minerals give it a characteristic blue colour. It is used widely as an ornamental facing stone.

Limestone a rock usually formed in warm shallow seas and composed of the mineral calcite ($CaCO_3$). Limestones are usually fossiliferous and fossils are sometimes abundant.

Magma Molten rock from the Earth's interior, which cools and solidifies to form *igneous rocks*.

Magmatic Relating to, or derived from, magma.

Marine transgression A marine transgression occurs when an influx of the sea covers areas of previously exposed land. Transgressions tend to be caused by the land subsiding.

Micaceous Containing the mineral mica.

Mudstone A fine-grained sedimentary rock originally composed of clay or mud.

Ooidal descriptive term for a limestone containing ooids, or spherical to ellipsoidal grains of carbonate that are generally 0.25–2.00 mm in diameter.

Oxygen isotopes The ratio of two isotopes of oxygen that are present in some substances, such as polar ice or calcite in ocean core samples, is linked to water temperature of ancient oceans, which in turn reflects ancient climates.

Periglacial A term applied to the climate of the region adjacent to an ice sheet. Such areas are likely to be permanently snow covered with ground frost to some depth (permafrost).

Pyroclastic flow A rapid avalanching of ash and rock fragments down the flanks of an erupting volcano.

Quartz The crystalline form of silica (silicon dioxide, SiO_2).

Quartzose Term applied to sands and sandstones that are essentially composed of quartz.

Refractory A material that retains its strength at high temperatures, usually above 1000°F (538°C).

Sandstone A sedimentary rock composed of sand-sized grains (i.e. generally visible to the eye, but less than 2 mm in size). *Volcaniclastic sandstone* is where all of the grains are of volcanic origin.

Sedimentary rock A rock that is commonly formed by the binding together (lithification) of sediment particles (e.g. *sandstone*, *siltstone*, *mudstone*).

Siltstone A sedimentary rock composed of silt-sized grains (i.e. only just visible to the eye).

Subcrop An area where an older formation and contained structures, such as faults, occurs directly below an unconformity.

Superficial deposits Material laid down in geologically very recent times as a loose (unconsolidated) mantle across the bedrock.

Trace fossils Structures in sedimentary rocks that are the result of activity by living organisms. They include burrows, footprints, tracks, trails, evidence of feeding and resting.

Tuff A collective term for consolidated pyroclastic rocks (i.e. rocks formed directly from volcanic eruptions) with fragments less than 64 mm in mean diameter.

Unconformity A surface of contact between two rock units, which represents a time gap in the geological record, usually due to a combination of erosion (*erosional unconformity*), *tectonic* activity and a cessation of sedimentation.

Volcaniclastic A general term for rocks composed wholly or in part of volcanic fragments i.e. fragments originating from volcanic eruptions (*pyroclastic material*) or from the erosion of volcanoes (*epiclastic material*).

USEFUL INFORMATION

How to get to The National Forest

The National Forest lies in western Leicestershire, south Derbyshire and eastern Staffordshire. The main north–south routes crossing the area are the M1 crossing the eastern part (exit at junctions 22 or 23), the A42 the central part (exit Junction 11 at the end of the M42, Measham or Ashby-de-la-Zouch) and the A38 in the western part (several exits between Burton upon Trent and Alrewas), making access by car very easy. The A6 also runs north–south just east of the Forest. The main east–west routes are the A50 just to the north of the Forest, and the A511 within the Forest.

There is a very good network of roads within The National Forest and good bus services. Railway stations at Burton upon Trent, Loughborough and Leicester also provide easy access to the Forest. The main visitor centre for The National Forest is Conkers at Moira; other visitor centres include Rosliston Forestry Centre and Snibston Discovery Park at Coalville.

Tourist Information

Burton upon Trent
Market Place, High Street,
Burton upon Trent, DE14 1AH
Tel: +44 (0)1283 508 000

Coalville
Snibston Discovery Park, Ashby Road,
Coalville, LE67 3LN
Tel: +44 (0)1530 813 608

Ashby-de-la-Zouch
North Street, Ashby-de-la-Zouch,
LE65 1HU
Tel: +44 (0)1530 411 767

Leicester
7/9 Every Street, Town Hall Square,
Leicester, LE1 6AG
Tel: +44 (0)116 299 8888

Loughborough
Loughborough Town Hall, Market Place,
Loughborough, LE11 3EB
Tel: +44 (0)1509 218 113

Derby
Assembly Rooms, Market Place,
Derby, DE1 3AH
Tel: +44 (0)1332 255802

Tamworth
29 Market Street, Tamworth, B79 7LR
Tel: +44 (0)1827 709581/709618

Lichfield
Lichfield Garrick, Castle Dyke,
Lichfield, WS13 6HR
Tel: +44 (0)1543 412112

In addition, information can be obtained from a number of websites including:

www.nationalforest.org

www.landshapes.org

www.goleicestershire.com

www.visitderbyshire.co.uk

www.thisisstaffordshire.co.uk

www.visitheartofengland.com

www.information-britain.co.uk

www.aboutbritain.com/tourist-information-centres/leicestershire-tourist-informationcentres.

www.heritagebritain.com/county/Leicestershire.html

www.bgs.ac.uk

Further reading

For more detailed accounts of the geology of the area:

GEOLOGY OF THE COALVILLE DISTRICT (2010). Compiled by Poul Strange, John Carney and Keith Ambrose. *Sheet Explantion of the British Geological Survey, Sheet 155.* ISBN 978-085272634-1.

GEOLOGY OF THE LOUGHBOROUGH DISTRICT (2002). Compiled by John Carney, Keith Ambrose and Allan Brandon. *Sheet Explantion of the British Geological Survey, Sheet 141.* ISBN 0 85272 411 X.

GEOLOGY OF THE COUNTRY BETWEEN LOUGHBOROUGH, BURTON AND DERBY (2001). Compiled by John Carney, Keith Ambrose and Allan Brandon. *Sheet Description of the British Geological Survey, Sheet 141.* ISBN 0 85272 388.

GEOLOGY OF THE COUNTRY AROUND COALVILLE (1988). By Bernard Worssam and Robin Old. *Memoir of the British Geological Survey, Sheet 155.* ISBN 0 11 884398.

GEOLOGY OF THE COUNTRY BETWEEN BURTON UPON TRENT, RUGELEY AND UTTOXETER (1955). By Ian Stevenson and George Mitchel. *Memoir of the Geological Survey of Great Britain, Sheet 140.*

BRITISH REGIONAL GEOLOGY: CENTRAL ENGLAND. By Brian Haynes and Albert Horton. London HMSO for Institute of Geological Sciences. ISBN 0 11 880088 4.

THE GEOLOGY OF THE EAST MIDLANDS (1968). By Peter Sylvester-Bradley and Trevor Ford. (Leicester: Leicester University Press.) ISBN 7185 1072 0.

Coal mining

THE LEICESTERSHIRE AND SOUTH DERBYSHIRE COALFIELD, 1200–1900 (1984). By Colin Owen, Moorland Publishing Co. Ltd. ISBN: 0 86190124 X.

ROUND AND ROUND A LOT MORE COAL STILL UNDERGROUND. THE COLLIERIES OF THE EASTERN BASIN OF THE LEICESTERSHIRE/DERBYSHIRE COALFIELD (2009). By Keith Gilliver, Gullavain Publishing.

THERE'S STILL MORE COAL IN TH'OLE. THE COLLIERIES OF THE WESTERN BASIN OF THE LEICESTERSHIRE DERBYSHIRE COALFIELD (2007). By Keith Gilliver, Gullavain Publishing.

GETTING THE COAL. IMPRESSIONS OF A TWENTIETH CENTURY MINING COMMUNITY (1992). By Jeanne Carswell and Tracey Roberts. The Alden Press, Oxford. ISBN: 0 9515040 1 0.

Walking

EXPLORING THE LANDSCAPE OF CHARNWOOD FOREST AND MOUNTSORREL (2007). By Keith Ambrose. Published by the British Geological Survey.

WALKING IN CHARNWOOD (1997). By Heather MacDermid. Published by Cordee. ISBN 1 871890 18 17.

A GEOLOGICAL WALK AROUND BRADGATE PARK (2004). By Annette McGrath. Published by the British Geological Survey.

A GEOLOGICAL WALK AROUND CLIFFE HILL QUARRY (2004). By Annette McGrath. Published by the British Geological Survey.

General

HERITAGE IN THE MAKING. THE NATIONAL FOREST (2006). By James Parry. This book spans 10 000 years of the history of the landscape that became The National Forest, and also looks at the people who helped to create that landscape. Published by the National Forest Company.

Further information

The British Geological Survey, at Keyworth near Nottingham has a shop selling many geological publications, jewellery, rocks, minerals and fossils and various items manufactured in stone. The British Geological Survey have produced a map, booklet and DVD/video on the Geology of Charnwood Forest. This has been aimed at A Level students and can be obtained from the online shop at the BGS website, www. bgs.ac.uk.

There are two local geological societies that can provide information: the East Midlands Geological Society www.emgs.org.uk and the Leicester Literary and Philosophical Society www.le.ac.uk/litandphil. In addition, The Russell Society (www.russellsoc.org) organises visits to study and collect minerals, particularly those found in the quarries of Charnwood Forest. Information on The National Forest can be obtained from www.nationalforest.org.

Acknowledgements

This book and map have been produced by the British Geological Survey, funded by the Defra Aggregates Levy Sustainability Fund through the Minerals Industry Research Organisation (MIRO). The map was compiled and the book written by Keith Ambrose, Poul Strange and Graham Lott of the British Geological Survey, Annette McGrath and Sam Lattaway of The National Forest Company and by Gill Weightman (Weightman Associates). The archaeology was written by Peter Liddle (Leicestershire), Dave Barrett (Derbyshire) and Stephen Dean (Staffordshire). Caron Simpson, Bob Cooper and Tony Clifton are thanked for their cartographic input. Thanks also to Gill Weightman who tested the walks in addition to the authors. The book was edited by Joanna Thomas and John Carney of the British Geological Survey and designed by Amanda Hill. Tom Hose kindly read through the final draft text and made numerous helpful comments.

The photographs are derived from a number of sources, mainly the British Geological Survey and The National Forest Company. Unless stated otherwise photographs are BGS © NERC. The National Railway museum is thanked for supplying a photograph; Noel Worley (British Gypsum) is thanked for supplying photographs and plan of the works of the Fauld mine; Tony Waltham is thanked for supplying a photograph of the Fauld crater. The Whitwick Historical Group is thanked for supplying a photograph of an old postcard from Whitwick Quarry; Aggregate Industries are thanked for supplying historical photographs of Bardon Hill Quarry from their archive at the quarry; Midland Quarry Products are thanked for supplying historical photographs from Old Cliffe Hill Quarry; UK Coal are thanked for supplying a historical photograph of Hick's Lodge opencast coal site; The National Brewery Centre in Burton upon Trent is thanked for supplying historical photographs from its archive.

Keith Ambrose, Poul Strange and Graham Lott publish with permission of the Executive Director, British Geological Survey (NERC).